Active Teaching and Learning Approaches in SCIENCE

Centre for Science Education, Sheffield City Polytechnic

Collins Educational

An imprint of HarperCollins*Publishers*

Collins Educational
An imprint of HarperCollins*Publishers*
77–85 Fulham Palace Road
London W6 8JB

© Sheffield City Polytechnic 1992

First published 1992. Reprinted 1994

ISBN 0 00 327829 8

Printed in Great Britain by Redwood Books, Trowbridge

Note: At the time of publication Sheffield City Polytechnic were seeking to change their name to Sheffield Hallam University, subject to Privy Council ratification.

Designed by Derek Lee
Artwork by Juliet and Charles Snape. Additional illustrations by Shaun MacGarry.

Special thanks are given to Sue Williams, Project Editor, whose ceaseless efforts and boundless enthusiasm helped make this publication possible. Sadly, Sue passed away in 1992.

Acknowledgements

Every effort has been made to contact the holders of copyright material, but if any have been inadvertently overlooked the publishers will be pleased to make the necessary arrangements at the first opportunity.
The authors and publishers are grateful to the following for permission to reproduce text and illustrations: Association for Science Education; Basil Blackwell Ltd; Heinemann Educational; HMSO©; Hutchinson Books Ltd; Kogan Page Ltd; School Examinations and Assessment Council.

Project Team

Project Director: Bill Harrison, Head of Centre for Science Education, Sheffield City Polytechnic.
Project Editors: Susan Williams and Terry Hudson, Centre for Science Education, Sheffield City Polytechnic; Derek Green, Head of Science, Wisewood School, Sheffield.
Advisers: Ken Mannion, Adviser, Barnsley LEA; Roy Phipps, Lecturer in Science Education, University of Durham; Mark Windale, Clifton Comprehensive School, Rotherham.

Major Contributors

Viv Bates; Head of Chemistry, Tapton School, Sheffield; Sally Beeston, Education Officer, BBC radio; John Coulton, Head of Science, Yewlands School, Sheffield; Dick Downie, Head of Planning, Yorkshire and Humberside Arts; Velda Harris, formerly, Senior Lecturer, Division of Communication Studies and English, Sheffield City Polytechnic; Vic Lally, Lecturer, Division of Education, Sheffield University; Colin Martin, Curriculum and Assessment Resource, Sheffield LEA; Bryan Milner, Educational Consultant, Ronsay Education Services, Ronsay; John Murphy, Head of Science, North Border School, Doncaster; Kevin O'Shea and Peter Sellwood, National Problem Solving 5–13 Project; Chrissie Poulter, Lecturer in Drama, Trinity College, University of Dublin; Dave Sant, Problem Solving with Industry Project Officer, Centre for Science Education, Sheffield City Polytechnic; Graham Scott, Kinetic Theatre Company; Anne Suffolk, Education Officer, Central TV; Richard Sykes, Technical Writer, Economics Ltd, Sheffield; David Walker, SATIS Evaluator; Richard Walton, Senior Lecturer, Centre for Science Education, Sheffield City Polytechnic; John Wardle, NCET; Jerry Wellington, Senior Lecturer, Division of Education, Sheffield University; Michael Whitemore, Kinetic Theatre Company.

The project team and publishers would also like to thank the following for their contributions:

Chris Baker, Peter Best, Peter Bishton, Steve Bradshaw, Dave Brodie, Russell Burton, Steve Chambers, Boo Clarke, David Colledge, Peter Douglas, Graham Eaton, Richard Forder, Rod Francis, David Harker, Rebekah Hodson, Ian Hylan, Mike Januszewski, Phil Lidstone, Geoff Lloyd, Ruth Marsh, Alan Monks, Janet Morgan, Kevin Mortan, Adrian Pickles, Keith Salisbury, Mike Smith, Andrew Warren, David Wilde.

Contents

Preface

Active teaching and learning approaches in science is in every sense a curriculum development project. It has drawn upon the expertise, experience, advice, enthusiasm, ideas and suggestions of over 50 science and non-science teachers, educators and expert practitioners from around the country. We hope that the fusion of active teaching and learning methods, ideas and skills has worked successfully.

In recent years, there has been a considerable growth of interest in active learning, largely fuelled by projects such as Children's Learning in Science (CLIS) and Science and Technology in Society (SATIS), both of which have informed our work. The SATIS evaluation study has been particularly useful and, along with our own surveys, has reinforced our view that teacher support for active learning will be greatly welcomed.

Many factors contribute to effective teaching and learning. However, in developing the material for this book we have been guided by two simple, yet we feel, important principles. First, children learn best when they are motivated to learn, i.e. when they find the learning experience enjoyable and worthwhile, and when they are actively involved in the learning process. Second, a teacher is likely to be more effective having first gained the confidence and skills to use a range of strategies which provide a variety of active learning experiences for the students. Therefore, we have tried to provide a wealth of ideas, strategies and practical classroom advice for active teaching and learning. We hope that you will find the book useful to dip into on a regular basis.

Over 30 student copymaster activities are included at the back of this book. These relate to the strategies covered in the teachers' chapters, and are intended to support these. As a basis for writing the copymasters, we initially asked students what type of activities they most enjoyed doing. To this end, we devised (and fully trialled) all the copymasters. They include: simple puzzles and games; problems and investigations; activities for visits and receiving visitors; activities using audio and video techniques; active reading and creative writing; data handling. We have also tried to ensure that knowledge and understanding gained from such activities is applied in a new situation so that the activity is not just an end in itself. As well as developing scientific knowledge and understanding we feel that the copymasters encourage a wide range of other important and desirable skills to be developed and reinforced during science lessons.

We do hope you enjoy using this book and that it helps to make the teaching and learning of science in the National Curriculum a stimulating and active experience.

The project team would like to thank the following for their help, encouragement and support. First, we are indepted to Chris Blake, formerly Unwin Hyman Educational, whose enthusiasm and confidence in us enabled the project to get underway. We are also grateful to Dr David Mewthorpe, Director of the School of Science, Sheffield City Polytechnic, for his support and encouragement, and to Stuart Gill, Collins Educational, for his understanding and patience. Finally, we would like to thank all those teachers who have contributed, suggested ideas and commented on the materials.

Bill Harrison (Project Director)
(on behalf of the project team)

Strategy icons

For easy reference purposes, the teaching and learning strategies discussed in the teacher's chapters are each identified by a simple icon. The icons are used to identicate which of these strategies are tackled in the student copymasters at the back of this book. The principle strategy a copymaster addresses is shown using a black icon. Other strategies the activities cover are printed in grey. The icons are:

 Group discussion

 Role play and drama

 Problem-solving

 Active reading

 Information technology

 Video and audio tape recordings

 Active writing

 Visits, visitors and field trips

 Games and simulations

 Presentation

 Data handling

1

Introduction

Who is this manual for?

Quickly work through the flow diagram to see whether active teaching and learning will be of use to you.

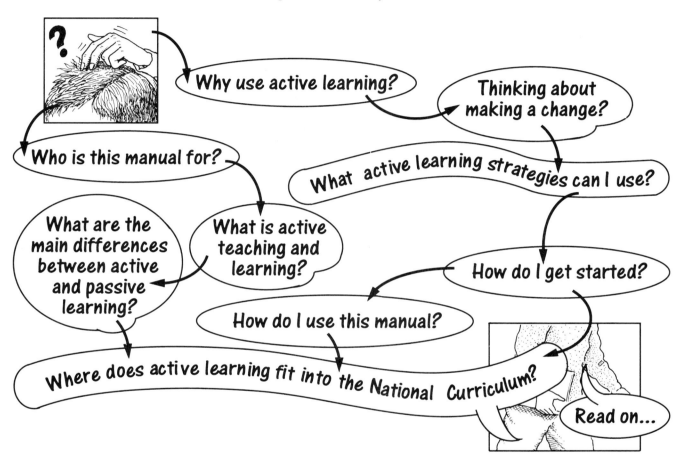

What is active teaching and learning?

The following lists the major characteristics generally associated with active teaching and learning.

Active **learning** takes place when students:

- have personal involvement in their learning,
- make decisions about the outcome of their work,
- own their work,
- test their own ideas,
- plan and design their own experiments,

- report their results to the rest of the class,
- evaluate their results,
- solve problems,
- discuss and interact purposefully in groups,
- reflect on the work they have done and reformulate their ideas.

Active **teaching** takes place when the teacher:

- encourages student responsibility for learning,
- gets students to think for themselves,
- offers a wide range of learning opportunities and strategies,
- encourages any activities that lead to the active learning situations described above.

ACTIVITY 1.1
Look at the classroom situations depicted. Discuss with other colleagues which examples you feel are active learning. Check your views with the ones listed – do you agree?

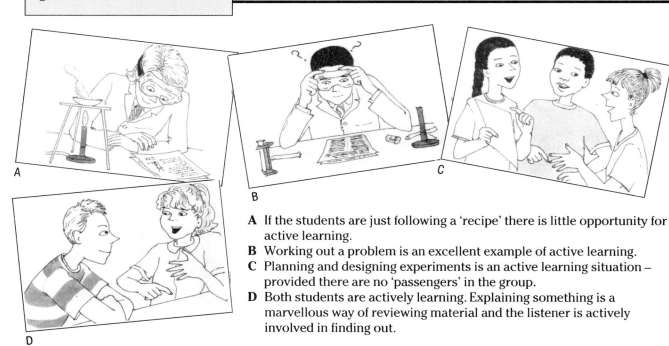

A If the students are just following a 'recipe' there is little opportunity for active learning.

B Working out a problem is an excellent example of active learning.

C Planning and designing experiments is an active learning situation – provided there are no 'passengers' in the group.

D Both students are actively learning. Explaining something is a marvellous way of reviewing material and the listener is actively involved in finding out.

Why use active learning?

Active learning techniques frequently can enable students to attain a higher level of understanding in science than with more traditional passive learning approaches. The key to this is a sense of ownership and personal involvement that active learning creates. Students see their work as important because **they** feel important and **their** ideas and findings are valued. Student satisfaction is enhanced and there is greater motivation.

Active learning strategies enable teachers to spend more time with individuals and small groups in order to encourage, assist, advise, monitor and record. Teachers can give more attention to the special needs of students and respond to the National Curriculum criteria for individual learning programmes. The strategies are crucial to the implementation of the aims of the Technical, Vocational and Educational Initiative (TVEI) and TVEI (extension) which include a greater emphasis on developing the initiative, motivation and problem-solving skills of students.

Active learning can also help the development of equal opportunities for students. Small group discussion work can provide a more agreeable environment for shy students. Group presentation of experimental investigations enhances access and role satisfaction for students of **all** abilities. Group cooperation amongst students acts positively against divisions which often exist for race or gender reasons. Mutual respect is encouraged.

On a more pragmatic note active learning strategies can aid the monitoring and recording of student progress through the National Curriculum. It is clear there will be a need to create opportunities for assessment during normal lesson time, and moving to a more student-centred resource-based learning environment will make this easier. Active learners take on more responsibility for their own learning.

Thinking about making a change?

The table examines the barriers to active teaching and some of the pathways through them. Whilst it is unlikely that your teaching will promote only one style of learning, if you intend to include more student-centred active learning in your lessons we hope this manual will help you to do so.

Barriers	Pathways
Change of role and loss of status. Are students getting the right information?	Allow students more responsibility for their own learning. Don't be the font of knowledge.
New teaching strategies need to be learned.	This can be challenging and stimulating, and enables personal growth for both teacher and student. Do some reading, get some training – try it!
Suspicion and cynicism among colleagues.	Talk to colleagues; tell them about the successes.
Chaos, uproar, confusion; discipline problems.	Ground rules set by teacher and students together. Engender student responsibility and self-discipline. Value their views and establish trust.
Time-consuming.	Initially maybe, but accept that important skills are being developed.

So what are the main differences between active and passive learning?

Teacher-centred passive learning is characterised by:

- teacher exposition,
- accent on competition,
- whole-class teaching,
- teacher responsible for the learning,
- teacher providing knowledge,
- students seen as empty vessels which need filling up,
- subject knowledge valued,
- teacher-imposed discipline,
- teacher and student roles stressed,
- teacher decides curriculum,
- passive student roles,
- limited range of learning styles and activities.

Student-centred active learning is characterised by:

- group work,
- accent on cooperation,
- resource-based learning,
- student takes responsibility for learning,
- teacher is a guide/facilitator,
- student ownership of ideas and work,
- process skills are valued,
- self-discipline,
- students seen as a source of knowledge and ideas,
- students involved in curriculum planning,
- students actively involved in learning,
- wide range of learning styles employed.

The above is based on ideas suggested in D. Brandes and P. Ginnis *A Guide to Student Centred Learning* (Basil Blackwell, 1986).

How do I get started?

Many of the active learning strategies in this manual echo similar techniques used at every level in educational establishments. In all these institutions the early introduction of such techniques is encouraged so that students develop skills and confidence over a period of time. It is beneficial to introduce active learning strategies with year-seven students, who may well have had recent experiences of similar teaching methods, rather than year-ten students who feel more inhibited and self-conscious.

Try to:
- be realistic about the situations you present to students and the outcomes you expect,
- begin with a short activity and a simple task,
- extend existing teaching methods, e.g. if you run group discussions make these more student led,
- prepare yourself for limited initial success. Students need to acquire the necessary skills progressively over a period of time. (You may find your efforts are part of a school policy on active learning, encompassing the whole curriculum.)

What active learning strategies can I use?

There are many active learning strategies available and each one is considered in this manual:

ACTIVE LISTENING — READING

ACTIVE LEARNING STRATEGIES

DARTS
Debating
Small group discussion
Teacher practical demonstration
Brainstorming
Problem-solving
Interviewing
Surveys
CAL

Science diaries
Reports
Formal presentation
Design
Visits
Simulations
Visitors
Role play
Fieldwork
Posters
Games
Case studies
Creative writing
Drama

TALKING — MANIPULATING — WRITING

Where does active learning fit into the National Curriculum?

The National Curriculum is an individual entitlement and active learning strategies help all individuals to achieve their maximum potential within the curriculum.

Active learning allows students to develop their abilities to plan, hypothesise and predict; design and carry out investigations; draw inferences and communicate exploratory tasks and experiments within the National Curriculum. This form of learning also increases understanding of the knowledge and content in the National Curriculum. Specifically, active learning involving reflection on activities and experiments carried out by students helps them to understand the way their scientific ideas are changing in the light of new evidence. This, in turn, leads to an understanding in more general terms of the development and use of scientific ideas.

How do I use this manual?

ACTIVITY 1.2
Quickly jot down the active learning strategies you wish to study and then head for the appropriate chapter!

The manual is designed to enable you to proceed quickly to the particular active learning strategy you wish to use. Each chapter begins with a chart which outlines its content. Consideration is then given as to why the learning strategy is useful. Ways of using the strategy are set out after this.

2

Study skills

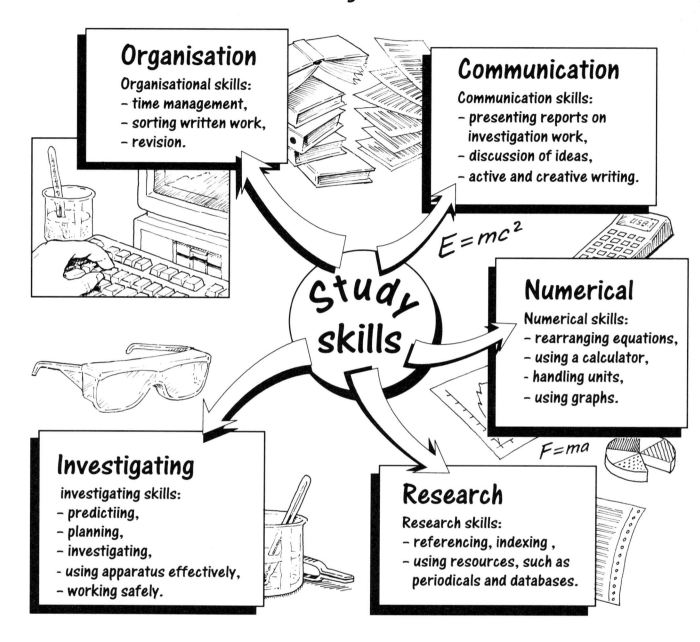

Organisation

Organisational skills:
- time management,
- sorting written work,
- revision.

Communication

Communication skills:
- presenting reports on investigation work,
- discussion of ideas,
- active and creative writing.

$E = mc^2$

Numerical

Numerical skills:
- rearranging equations,
- using a calculator,
- handling units,
- using graphs.

$F = ma$

Investigating

investigating skills:
- predictiing,
- planning,
- investigating,
- using apparatus effectively,
- working safely.

Research

Research skills:
- referencing, indexing ,
- using resources, such as periodicals and databases.

Why develop study skills in science lessons?

Acquiring study skills allows the student to become an effective **independent** learner. This does not make the teacher redundant but enables the student to make better use of a vast range of resources, including the teacher! The student gains confidence and becomes more aware of the processes and personal involvement that lead to success. Such skills need developing gradually throughout a student's schooling.

Students need to acquire study skills in order to satisfy some of the requirements of the exploration of science element in the National Curriculum.

ACTIVITY 2.1
Try a brainstorm (see page 32) on the factors affecting independent learning. Ring those factors which you think are helped by improving study skills.

What sort of study skills are relevant to science students?

Study the table:

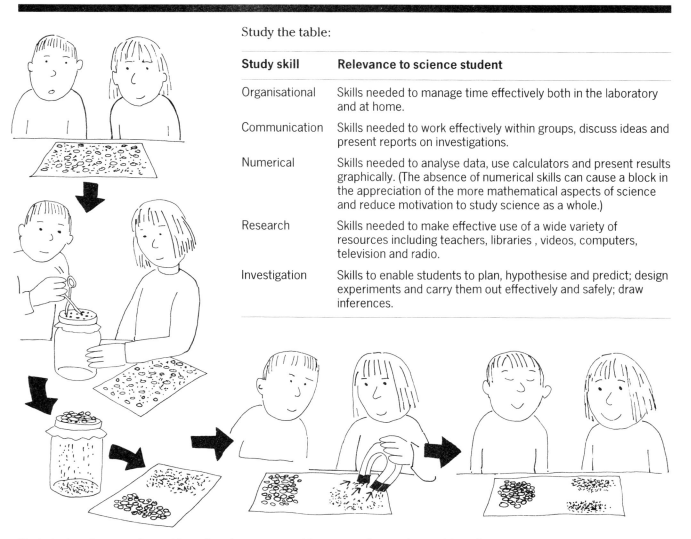

Study skill	Relevance to science student
Organisational	Skills needed to manage time effectively both in the laboratory and at home.
Communication	Skills needed to work effectively within groups, discuss ideas and present reports on investigations.
Numerical	Skills needed to analyse data, use calculators and present results graphically. (The absence of numerical skills can cause a block in the appreciation of the more mathematical aspects of science and reduce motivation to study science as a whole.)
Research	Skills needed to make effective use of a wide variety of resources including teachers, libraries , videos, computers, television and radio.
Investigation	Skills to enable students to plan, hypothesise and predict; design experiments and carry them out effectively and safely; draw inferences.

Students do not necessarily need to *write* a clear report, as this account of separating a mixture shows.

Which study skills does this chapter concentrate on?

We shall examine all the above study skills and how they may be (actively) encouraged. Many of the study skills are dealt with in greater depth in later chapters. For example, the chapters on group discussion, active reading, active writing and presentation cover many aspects of communication.

Using the strategy

Organisational skills

Disorganised students are at a tremendous disadvantage once they have to accept responsibility for their own work. Organisation skills can be actively fostered using the techniques described here.

Time management

Time management can help students who are particularly slow at getting started or who never seem to finish experiments. Awareness of time can be heightened using the following activities:

- A timed problem-solving exercise, e.g. design and test a way to keep 500 centimetres of boiled water in a beaker as hot as possible for 10 minutes. (Remember to supply insulating materials.)
- Ask groups to record how long they spend on each part of an experiment, i.e. planning, collecting apparatus, setting-up, doing the experiment, recording and presenting results. It is important that this activity is not treated as a race but as an opportunity to identify ways of improving organisation.

'Putting-off' (or displacement) activities are universal – the desperate urge for a cup of coffee seems to manifest itself each time a pile of marking needs doing! Students are not immune to this behaviour either, particularly when original thought is required, e.g. in planning experiments. Motivation is obviously the key but developing student awareness of the tendency to put-off also helps.

ACTIVITY 2.2

Try a 10 minute class brainstorm on ways used to put off doing homework. Generate ideas on how to overcome these and discuss the most conducive conditions for study.

Sorting written work

Student folders and notebooks range from the immaculately ordered to the totally chaotic, particularly if activities generate both theoretical and experimental notes. Worksheets, notes, problems, reports, etc. need categorising and highlighting if genuinely helpful records are to be made. Encourage the use of colour-coding, labelling, summarising, cross-referencing, indexing, dividers, etc.

ACTIVITY 2.3

Try a group activity on deciding the important points in a piece of text, and how to highlight them. Devise questions to help groups find these if necessary. (A follow-up class discussion comparing the points considered to be important is a useful way of gaining consensus.)

- Prioritising points and highlighting text can be extended to the student's notebook or file. The student may decide to highlight all laws in a particular way and all equations in another. Highlighting techniques, if not over done, can help organisation and the revision process later.

> A box around a sentence can make it stand out.

Alternatively you can put stars in the margin, or leave a space. Simple <u>underlining</u> also helps, but some people prefer highlighting with coloured pens, or fancy boxes:

- At the end of a topic the production of a group report is a useful summary. Individual summaries entered into notebooks help with the organisation of other material.
- Some students find diagrams assist recall and are much easier to study. Spider charts specifically drawn to summarise sections of work can prove invaluable. Spider charts make useful summaries, and are particularly effective at showing the links between different parts of a topic. Making spider charts can be:
  - a group activity leading to posters for comparison between groups,
  - a teacher-led class brainstorm,
  - an individual student activity.

ACTIVITY 2.4

Create a spider chart for a topic of your choice. Compare it to the one shown.

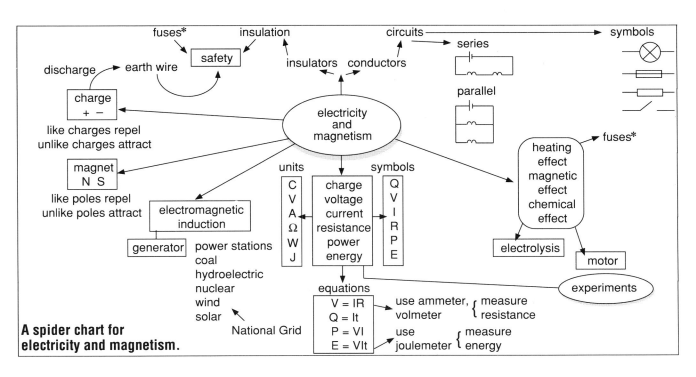

A spider chart for electricity and magnetism.

The spider chart shows "electricity and magnetism" at the centre with branches to:

- fuses* → safety ← insulation
- insulators, conductors
- circuits → series, parallel → symbols
- discharge → earth wire → safety
- charge + − : like charges repel, unlike charges attract
- magnet N S : like poles repel, unlike poles attract
- electromagnetic induction → generator
- power stations: coal, hydroelectric, nuclear, wind, solar → National Grid
- units: C V A Ω W J
- charge, voltage, current, resistance, power, energy
- symbols: Q V I R P E
- equations:
  - $V = IR$
  - $Q = It$
  - $P = VI$
  - $E = VIt$
  - use ammeter, voltmeter { measure resistance
  - use joulemeter { measure energy
- heating effect, magnetic effect, chemical effect → fuses*, electrolysis, motor, experiments

Revision

On the subject of GCSE revision it was quoted on a radio programme 'Our teacher's no good. She teaches us the stuff alright, but doesn't tell us how to revise.' This is a prime example of a student who recognises the need for guidance in effective revision. The study of review techniques and learning patterns can help students revise effectively in the limited time that is available for this process. Simple changes in revision technique can lead to dramatic improvements in both recall and application of knowledge. The following is suggested:

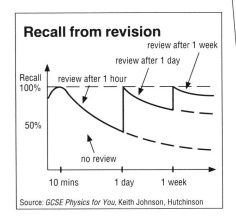

Recall from revision

Recall 100%

review after 1 hour
review after 1 day
review after 1 week

50%

no review

10 mins   1 day   1 week

Source: *GCSE Physics for You*, Keith Johnson, Hutchinson

Revision

- Encourage student awareness and responsibility for the revision process.
- Get students to organise their notebooks or files, and plan revision schedules.
- Suggest varied active revision techniques, e.g. tackling problems, making summaries, using computer assisted learning (CAL), or testing one another.
- Use past question papers for group activities on how to tackle exam questions.
- Discourage the 'night-before' syndrome. Organise a class discussion on the graph shown for improving recall by repeated short review patterns.

ACTIVITY 2.5
Discuss with your students what ideas they have for revision techniques. (You may find some students have been using similar techniques to the ones just described.)

The fractional recall after a single revision session is much greater if the work is divided into short sessions (say 30 minutes) with short, planned breaks in between. Recall is also improved if a quick summary is made of the work just done, after each short break. Repeated reviews of the same work vastly increases recall, as the graph shows.

Communication skills

There are three main areas to cover when dealing with student communication skills:

- presentation of findings from investigative work,
- discussion of ideas, either in a small group, a class discussion, or individually,
- active and creative writing.

We shall confine ourselves to the first of these skills in this chapter. Treatment of the other two can be found in chapter 3, Group discussion (talking and listening) and chapter 5, Active writing, respectively.

Presentation reports on experimental work

A formal framework can sometimes help students with experimental accounts but it is frequently misused or misunderstood. A rigid framework hinders free expression and the student's understanding and interpretation of the observations are often lost. The cry 'But what do I put in the conclusion?' illustrates only too clearly the failure of this approach.

The following strategies can help improve reporting skills:

Experimental reports
- Identify who the report is intended for. Will it be for the student's own purposes, or will it be read by other students or the teacher? Will the report be discussed?
- Ask students to write short personal accounts in their own style to develop ownership of work and increase motivation.
- Encourage class presentation of reports and subsequent discussion to build on their value and the activity leading to it.
- Cultivate the use of clearly labelled diagrams. Run activities on labelling if necessary.
- Encourage group reports on investigations such as short talks or presentations using posters, OHPs, tape recordings or even videos.

Read chapter 6, Presentation for more advice on presenting work.

Numerical skills

How often do you hear comments such as these: 'I can't do physics, it's too mathematical', 'I like the experiments but this working-out is hard'? Difficulty with mathematical concepts often creates additional barriers to effective scientific learning. Chapter 10, Data handling and interpretation, gives an in depth treatment of this area. However, a few common mathematical barriers are highlighted here:

Rearranging equations

Rearranging the simplest of equations can prove a major stumbling block to some students. This skill needs to be practised. Liaison with the mathematics department to make sure you speak the same 'language' and use the same strategies will help.

Treating an equation like a balanced see-saw and only doing to one side what is also done to the other ('being fair') can prove fruitful. Group activities using the being-fair approach to solving problems can help with difficulties. If students still find this difficult they may need to learn a simple equation in all its forms, e.g. $\text{density} = \dfrac{\text{mass}}{\text{volume}}$,

$\text{mass} = \text{density} \times \text{volume}$, and $\text{volume} = \dfrac{\text{mass}}{\text{density}}$

Using a calculator

The wrong button on a calculator is easily pressed, often giving ridiculous answers to calculations. Estimating the approximate answer before hitting a key is a useful technique to check calculator readings. Group discussion activities will give confidence at estimating. Another common error is reading numbers from the calculator which are not in common with the accuracy of the data entered. Group discussion is also needed on how accurately scales can be read. The correct number of figures to quote is soon realised.

Handling units

Difficulty in handling units can be symptomatic of the conceptual problems that science students have at all levels, e.g. difference between mass and weight, force and energy. Further problems occur when the unit is alien to common experience, e.g. pascals, newtons. Combinations of units from problem-solving and graphical analysis can be especially tricky. Get students to include units in each line of calculation to help eliminate difficulties. Activities finding missing units or pairing units with quantities can help to establish greater accuracy.

Using graphs

The following activities can help students who have problems drawing and interpreting graphs:

Graphs

- Group data handling exercises in which results displayed in a variety of graphs and charts are compared. Displayed reports reduce the preponderance of blobs and thick zig-zagged lines.
- Encourage smooth curve drawing. Less dexterous students find bendy-rulers a great help.

- It is useful for students to compare lines they have plotted from a set of experimental results with one plotted by computer software using the same results.
- A class activity in which groups make part of an enormous temperature scale to surround the laboratory gives a clear idea of linear scale. A variety of significant temperatures can be researched and plotted on the scale.

Research skills

A class brainstorm is an interesting way of finding out where students obtain scientific information. The sources may include radio, television, video, textbooks, library books, computer programmes, magazines, newspapers **and** their teachers. The ability to use a wide variety of resources provides students with the confidence to become an effective independent learner. Some students have a domestic background which already nurtures their spirit of enquiry, and supports research they do. Other students are disadvantaged and may lack the confidence to find out information for themselves. These will benefit most from the following activities:

- Activities on the use of indexes and content lists.
- Group structured activities which necessitate piecing information together from a wide variety of sources. All these should be available in the laboratory.
- Activities based on newspaper or magazine articles. These help bring a topic to life, e.g. analysis of European weather patterns during the past week using weather charts, forecasts and satellite pictures.
- Researching information from databases.

- Science periods in the school library can help with library research – often an awesome task. Public libraries might also be utilised.

Tasks that require research in public libraries need detailed liaison with librarians for obvious reasons – terminal depression can set in for the librarian when asked for 'something about teeth' for the twenty-fifth time! Second, librarians will often be pleased to arrange appropriate displays if requested in advance. Supply worksheets on the use of libraries, such as the following how-to-find-out chart.

1 What subject are you finding out about?	2 Go to	3 the subject index	4 This is in alphaetical order (A–Z).	5 Each subject in the box has a **Dewey** number.	6 e.g. towns 301.3, trains 625.2, trees 582	7 Find your Dewey number.
						8 Now go to

How to find out chart

15 Books on the shelves	14 See if you can find it!	13 Now you know what is in the resource centre.	12 It is in Dewey number order (000–999).	11 Books, slides, wallcharts, tapes	10 This is a list of resources in the resource centre.	9 the catalogue
16 Slides in the slide cabinet						
17 Wallcharts in the cabinet	18 Remember	19 Theme boxes full of information and pictures!	20 Don't forget	21 Use the index in the book.	22 Keep a list of the books you use (bibliography).	

> **ACTIVITY 2.6**
> List the reference resources available to students in your school. Construct a chart or flow diagram to help students use these resources.

Video, televison and radio broadcasts can also provide a rich source of information. Questionnaires on more active watching or listening of these permit effective use of the media. The use of videos and tapes interactively is growing – see Chapter 12, Video and audio tape recordings.

Investigation skills

Students must be able to plan, hypothesise and predict, design and carry out investigations and draw inferences – a formidable range of skills.

Planning

Planning investigations and designing experimental work can be a daunting task. The skills needed to plan an investigation within the bounds of time constraint and available equipment can be developed using relatively short problem-solving exercises:

Experimenting

Perhaps the most frequent obstacle to independent investigation is fear of the apparatus itself. Will it blow up? How do I do this without breaking it? Identify apparatus phobias. Frequently students feel too self-conscious or are afraid of using particular pieces of apparatus.

Practical skills are needed in handling apparatus productively and safely:

Remember: it is important to discuss the accuracy to which all readings can be read, and possible margins of error.

Using apparatus effectively

Does apparatus laid out on the bench look like a scrap-yard? Do electrical circuits resemble knitting? It is important to set out equipment so that it is easy to use and easy to see what is going on. Sadly, this is not always simple. Electrical experiments often suffer from miswiring and muddle. A useful question to stimulate accurate layout is 'Could someone else take over my experiment and see what is happening?'

Drawings of apparatus with connecting wires can be a useful intermediary stage between a circuit diagram and the actual apparatus. These should be produced by the teacher initially, and later in small groups by the students, as preparation for building circuits. Particularly excellent examples of layout can be exhibited by groups to the rest of the class.

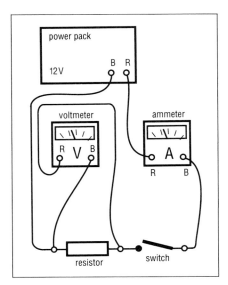

Working safely

Safety procedures are naturally of paramount importance in the science laboratory. If students are to work relatively independently in small groups they must be actively aware of safety procedures at all times. Give regular training and advice on safety.

Safety

- Ask students to produce group posters on laboratory safety.
- Hold games to match safety procedures to hazards.
- Make safety aspects a compulsory part of planning experiments.

ACTIVITY 2.7
List all the safety hazards you notice in the laboratory below. Now ask your students to do the same.

Safety in the lab?

3

Group discussion (Talking and listening)

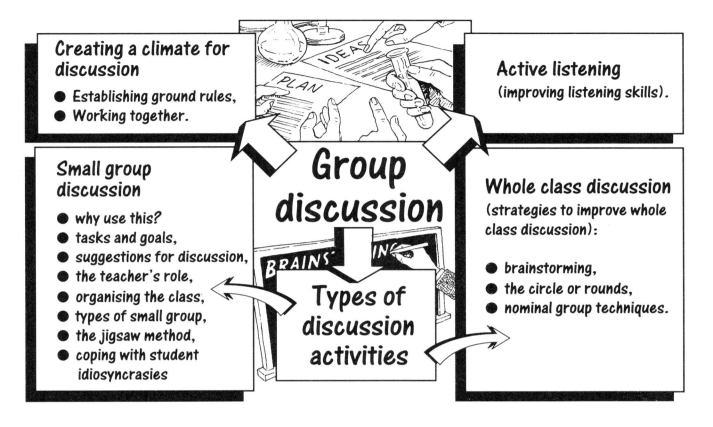

Creating a climate for discussion
- Establishing ground rules,
- Working together.

Active listening (improving listening skills).

Small group discussion
- why use this?
- tasks and goals,
- suggestions for discussion,
- the teacher's role,
- organising the class,
- types of small group,
- the jigsaw method,
- coping with student idiosyncrasies

Group discussion

Types of discussion activities

Whole class discussion (strategies to improve whole class discussion):

- brainstorming,
- the circle or rounds,
- nominal group techniques.

Introduction

Why use group discussion?

The essence of all successful group work is **purposeful** discussion.
Discussion helps students to explore their ideas, improve communication
skills, facilitate investigative group work, and encourage active
participation in the learning process.

Does much discussion work already exist in science?

Discussion work in school science has grown in importance during recent
years, largely fuelled by projects such as Science and Technology in
Society (SATIS) and Children's Learning in Science (CLIS), but also by the
inclusion of social aspects of science and technology in GCSE courses. A
further catalyst to discussion work has been the introduction of the
National Curriculum which emphasises the importance of investigations,
often carried out in small groups. Nevertheless, there is still a great deal of
teacher exposition in science education. Where there is too much teacher
domination there is little opportunity for students to explore ideas, or
follow arguments. Only a small minority of students may contribute to
lessons taught in this way.

Most science teachers recognise the value of classroom discussion and many wish to see it used more effectively in their lessons. It is important to develop the necessary skills for this. The aim of this chapter is to offer ideas and strategies for developing effective group discussion in science.

Using the strategy

Types of discussion activities

The type of active discussion activity can vary enormously. However, they can be broadly classified as below. It is quite possible to move from a discussion in one quadrant to a discussion in another, e.g. from guided discussion in pairs, to small group discussion, and then whole class discussion. You may wish to start a more structured discussion and move to a more open-ended, free-ranging discussion, or vice-versa.

Discussion activities

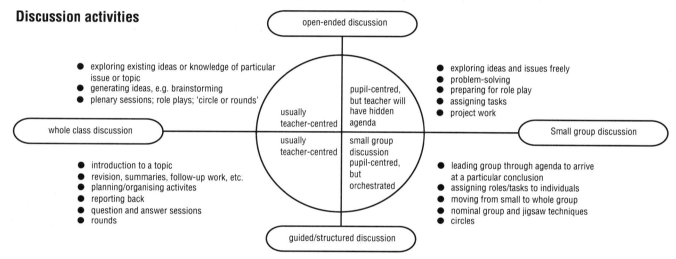

open-ended discussion

- exploring existing ideas or knowledge of particular issue or topic
- generating ideas, e.g. brainstorming
- plenary sessions; role plays; 'circle or rounds'

pupil-centred, but teacher will have hidden agenda

usually teacher-centred

- exploring ideas and issues freely
- problem-solving
- preparing for role play
- assigning tasks
- project work

whole class discussion

usually teacher-centred

small group discussion pupil-centred, but orchestrated

Small group discussion

- introduction to a topic
- revision, summaries, follow-up work, etc.
- planning/organising activites
- reporting back
- question and answer sessions
- rounds

- leading group through agenda to arrive at a particular conclusion
- assigning roles/tasks to individuals
- moving from small to whole group
- nominal group and jigsaw techniques
- circles

guided/structured discussion

Creating a climate for discussion

Before purposeful discussion can take place it is important to create the right climate or atmosphere in the classroom. Students need to develop a sense of trust, where everyone's opinion is listened to and respected; where anyone can choose not to speak; and where interruptions or ridicule are discouraged. It is helpful to establish accepted ground rules for this. The right atmosphere soon develops.

Try to:

- be open: tell students you are going to try out a new strategy,
- create a relaxed and friendly, yet organised and purposeful atmosphere,
- make the laboratory as conducive to discussion as possible,
- encourage open discussion,
- don't always bail students out,

- brainstorm the reasons for sharing decisions etc.,
- encourage students to have ownership and responsibility for their work,
- value what students have to say, even their mistakes,
- build trust and acceptance.

If you have not previously used much discussion work, try it out, but don't be too disappointed if it is not a roaring success initially. The students themselves will also be inexperienced in this technique, and need practise too. Perception of roles, teacher-student and student-student relationships, and the change in work pattern can all act as barriers to effective discussion. Some of the folowing ideas are suggested in D. Brandes and P. Ginnis, *A Guide to Student-centred Learning* (Basil Blackwell Ltd, 1986). The ideas apply to both small and whole group discussion and may be helpful.

Establishing the ground rules for group work

Student-centred active learning needs to be well structured and controlled. It is therefore important, particularly with larger groups, to establish ground rules at an early stage. What are the rules for establishing ground rules? There's really only one! **Get the group to establish the ground rules themselves.**

Compare your students' ground rules with the following suggested set of ground rules.

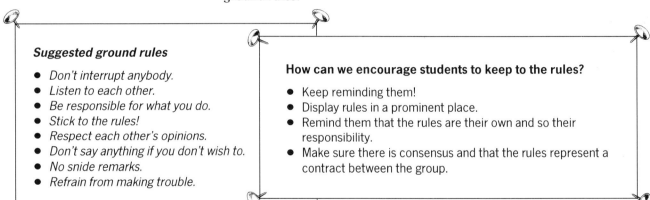

Suggested ground rules

- *Don't interrupt anybody.*
- *Listen to each other.*
- *Be responsible for what you do.*
- *Stick to the rules!*
- *Respect each other's opinions.*
- *Don't say anything if you don't wish to.*
- *No snide remarks.*
- *Refrain from making trouble.*

How can we encourage students to keep to the rules?

- Keep reminding them!
- Display rules in a prominent place.
- Remind them that the rules are their own and so their responsibility.
- Make sure there is consensus and that the rules represent a contract between the group.

The Waiting Game

- I'm not going to shout at them.
- I shall sit here quietly until I have their full attention.
- I'll tell them I will wait as long as it takes.
- Just relax; think about something pleasant – I mustn't look impatient.
- Ah! They're beginning to realise I'm playing the waiting game. They've seen me do this before.
- Good – others are joining in – and asking their friends to. They're beginning to see that it is their responsibility.

Working together

Disruptive tactics by one or two students within group discussion is to be expected. D. Brandes and H. Phillips, *Gamesters' Handbook* (Hutchinson, 1978) suggest it is worthwhile pre-empting this by introducing the concept of sabotage early on. Students learn to consider their own behaviour in relation to that of others, and soon realise the benefits of taking part rather than sabotaging. Sabotage is recognised more quickly, and students take responsibility for dealing with it. Discipline is shared between teacher and student.

Students must learn to draw on the collective intelligence of the group, sharing ideas and information. Agreement is reached by a combination of the following:

- evaluating all contributions,
- sorting and prioritising contributions,
- compromise,
- cooperation.

Active listening

We feel it is worth highlighting at this point, the importance of developing active listening skills as an essential component of discussion work. It is important that students can build on what others have said, to keep discussion flowing. No meaningful discussion can take place unless time is allowed for listening as well as talking. Too often we think someone communicates well because they speak well. The best communicators are also efficient listeners.

*According to D. Brandes and P. Ginnis, Student-centred Learning. An **active listener** should:*

- *sit quietly and look at the speaker,*
- *relax, and make any non-verbal responses that come naturally, e.g. nodding, or smiling,*

- *concentrate on listening and suspend all judgements and questions,*
- *make verbal responses that only reflect or paraphrase the main points discussed.*

As teachers we often think students are attentive when in fact they may be miles away or half asleep.

Wake up Jones! I've only been talking for half an hour.

Why doesn't he make it relevant to me?

Z-z-z-z

He's been talking non-stop for half an hour.

This is really boring.

He uses words I don't understand.

Why doesn't he speak up? I can't hear him.

I wish he'd stop tapping the bench and jingling his keys.

This is hard.

ACTIVITY 3.1
Brainstorm ways in which 'teacher-talk' can be improved to aid active listening. Getting yourself videoed or observed while teaching can be a daunting prospect, but if this is possible it can give valuable insight into your own teaching.

How can we improve students' listening skills?

There are a number of things we can do to encourage students to be more active listeners:

- Pose questions to a wide range of students.
- Ask students to make brief notes on a talk, demonstration, video, etc.
- Bring students around the front bench with note books. They will feel more involved in the proceedings.
- Move around the laboratory to get closer to students sitting further back.

- Practise active listening skills, e.g. begin a class discussion and then ask successive students to reflect on key phrases talked about before adding something of their own. Alternatively, try the 'moving circle' technique (see chapter 7 Role play and drama, page 57).

Active listening skills in small group work can be improved using a number of methods. A suitable introduction to the process of listening is to ask students to listen to you speak on a topic for fifteen minutes, and then follow this up with a brainstorm on what else students thought about while you were talking. This makes students aware of the concept of active listening, and its importance. Disuss with students how they feel when someone is obviously not listening to them, or get them to observe how other people listen (or don't listen), possibly in small groups.

Two other useful methods for improving listening skills are described here:

Twos and fours

Ask students to exchange information about a science topic in pairs. Join two pairs together and ask each person in turn to tell the other three what their respective partners told them. Students soon get an indication of how well each person listens.

Listening triads

Arrange students in groups of three and give each one a role: either speaker, questioner or recorder. The speaker comments on an issue or problem, and the questioner prompts or seeks clarification on what is being said. The recorder takes notes, and at the end of the conversation gives a brief report (just a few minutes long). The process is repeated with students swopping roles beforehand.

Small group discussion

Small group discussion (SGD) is undoubtedly one of the most powerful teaching and learning strategies we have at our disposal. It is quite possible that it may feature in every science lesson, so there are strong reasons for developing skills in its use.

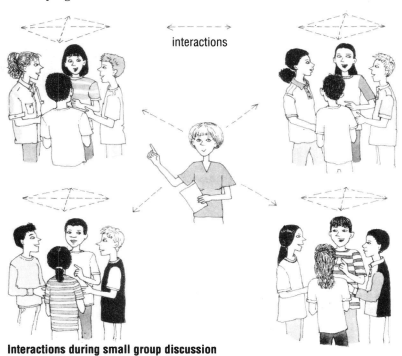

interactions

Interactions during small group discussion

ACTIVITY 3.2
Jot down what you think are the advantages and disadvantages of using small group discussion.

Why use small group discussion?

PROS

- maximises contributions,
- high student-student interactions,
- less threatening,
- students learn from each other,
- everyone can try out and share new ideas,
- enables students to explain and clarify points raised between each other,
- more imaginative and creative,
- less constrained by teacher-approved language,
- social skills are practised in a 'safe' environment, e.g. expressing views, tolerance, giving and receiving support, cooperation,
- responsibility for learning lies with group,
- discussion can be used to plan investigations, analyse results, and prepare for written work or report backs,
- increases self-awareness.

CONS

- time is needed to adjust to change in teacher and student roles,
- students may resist responsibility for their own learning,
- time is needed to develop cooperation and group participation skills,
- staff disapproval of new methods,
- lack of control, or confidence in new method,
- unease about the extent of learning taking place,
- learning initially difficult to assess,
- extra preparation often necessary, e.g. planning, grouping, tasks, agendas, etc.

The tasks and goals for discussion

The degree of structure of a group task dictates the extent of teacher management necessary. **Highly** structured tasks will clearly need less teacher direction. Examples of these are the structured discussion activities in SATIS units, e.g. *Living with kidney failure* and *Nuclear Power*, and tasks which involve practical work, problem-solving or decision-making (where group members have particular roles or there is an end product).

Less structured tasks involving the discussion of ideas or issues require more teacher direction, and for these we recommend the use of an agenda (see page 26).

The specific task a group is set is critical to effective discussion. The task should act as a focusing device for discussion, ultimately leading to a successful conclusion or goal.

The task must:

- initially be kept short,
- have a fixed time limit – tell students how much time they have,
- be straightforward to begin with; more open-ended problems can be set as group skills are developed,
- be relevant to the work in hand,
- have an attainable conclusion or goal.

The task should:

- have less structure if the discussion explores ideas, e.g. early stages of problem-solving,
- have more structure if you foresee a particular conclusion or goal. (Warning: rigid structures can stifle discussion.)

24

Some suggestions for small group discussion tasks

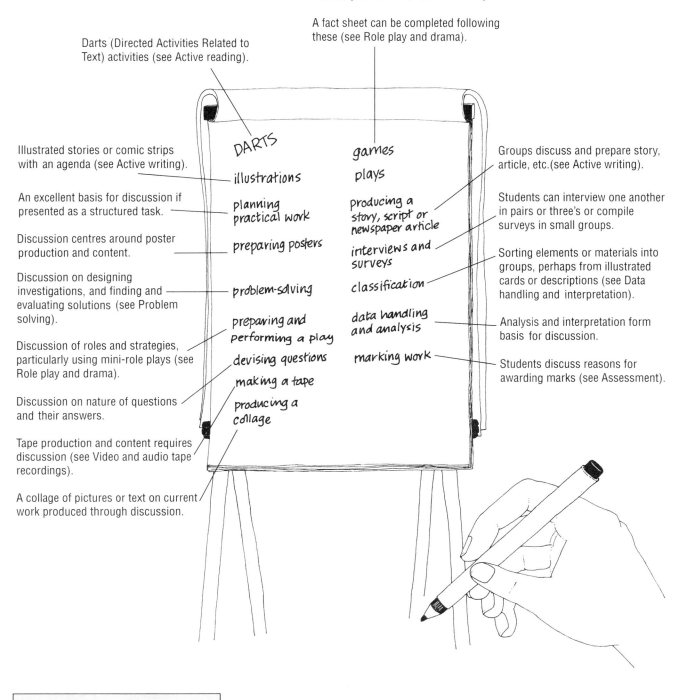

Darts (Directed Activities Related to Text) activities (see Active reading).

Discussion work on what has been learned (see Games and simulations).

A fact sheet can be completed following these (see Role play and drama).

Illustrated stories or comic strips with an agenda (see Active writing).

An excellent basis for discussion if presented as a structured task.

Discussion centres around poster production and content.

Discussion on designing investigations, and finding and evaluating solutions (see Problem solving).

Discussion of roles and strategies, particularly using mini-role plays (see Role play and drama).

Discussion on nature of questions and their answers.

Tape production and content requires discussion (see Video and audio tape recordings).

A collage of pictures or text on current work produced through discussion.

DARTS
games

illustrations
plays

planning
practical work
producing a story, script or newspaper article

preparing posters
interviews and surveys

problem-solving
classification

preparing and performing a play
data handling and analysis

devising questions
marking work

making a tape

producing a collage

Groups discuss and prepare story, article, etc.(see Active writing).

Students can interview one another in pairs or three's or compile surveys in small groups.

Sorting elements or materials into groups, perhaps from illustrated cards or descriptions (see Data handling and interpretation).

Analysis and interpretation form basis for discussion.

Students discuss reasons for awarding marks (see Assessment).

ACTIVITY 3.3
List examples of different activities suitable for small group discussion.

As we have said, less structured tasks require the use of an agenda to build step-by-step discussion:

- prepare the agenda,
- use the agenda to develop step-by-step discussion. Start in pairs, move on to fours, and finish with whole group discussion.

Consider the following agenda for a class who have just completed a practical session on testing solids, having previously investigated liquids and gases. You decide to spend the last twenty minutes of the lesson getting students to discuss their investigations in small groups. Your discussion agenda might look something like this:

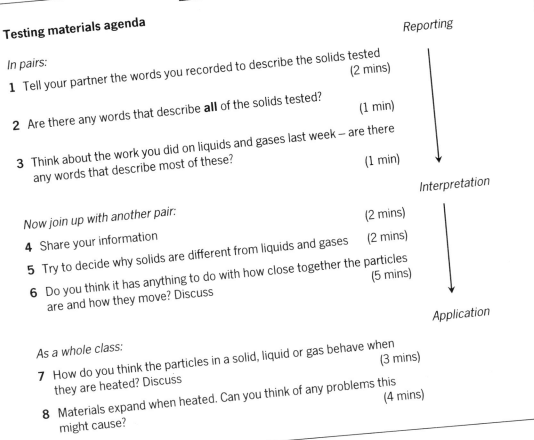

Testing materials agenda   *Reporting*

In pairs:

1 Tell your partner the words you recorded to describe the solids tested
(2 mins)

2 Are there any words that describe **all** of the solids tested?
(1 min)

3 Think about the work you did on liquids and gases last week – are there any words that describe most of these?
(1 min)

Interpretation

Now join up with another pair: (2 mins)

4 Share your information   (2 mins)

5 Try to decide why solids are different from liquids and gases

6 Do you think it has anything to do with how close together the particles
(5 mins)
are and how they move? Discuss

Application

As a whole class:

7 How do you think the particles in a solid, liquid or gas behave when
(3 mins)
they are heated? Discuss

8 Materials expand when heated. Can you think of any problems this
(4 mins)
might cause?

The discussion starts with pairs recalling facts and reporting on past experience. The teacher opens up the discussion by putting pairs into groups of four and continuing with questions 4–6. At this stage the teacher can **orchestrate** the discussion by encouraging contributions from different groups and sharing their ideas. In fact by controlling discussion between small groups the teacher is able to move back and forth from small group discussion to whole class discussion. Students feel confident at speaking in a whole class environment, because they have rehearsed their ideas in small groups. This allows **reflective** discussion to take place. More abstract ideas can be explored, with application of knowledge (questions 7–8). A formal reporting back to the whole class is optional, perhaps with group summary posters or overhead transparencies.

ACTIVITY 3.4
Jot down the different aspects of a teacher's role in small group discussion. Compare your ideas with those in the diagram.

26

The teacher's role in small group discussion

Ensure **reflective** discussion takes place. You may do this as group presentations to the whole class. If so, allow time for rehearsal in small groups:
● clarify points made,
● summarise and consolidate,
● share each groups' views,
● allow individuals to gain confidence by speaking to the whole class after rehearsing in their small group.

Have your own **agenda** but be prepared to be flexible. Make sure you have used a structured task or guided discussion with an agenda:
● consult groups on how they would like to tackle the task,
● allocate roles of jobs to students,
● rotate roles,
● be prepared to lead the class occasionally, reporting your own experiences.

Comment on group performance:
● the quality of their work,
● how they set about it,
● the role each played.

Have a sense of pace:
● move things forward, but allow pause for thought,
● don't be afraid of silences,
● be enthusiastic, lively and organised,
● create a relaxed atmosphere.

Get close to groups during discussion:
● suggest points missed **but do not take over**,
● bring timid or soft spoken students into the discussion,
● clarify points made **but do not reinterpret** them,
● value all views,
● constrain overdominant students,
● help crystallise arguments,
● note points for reflective discussion,
● ensure students both talk and listen.

Encourage group-to-group contributions
(this may lead to whole class discussion if desired):
● build up group loyalty by introducing a title,
● encourage friendly competition between small groups.

Organising classes for small group work

Group membership

- Use groups of three or four (maximum six).
- Allow a degree of self-selection initially, but tempered by your knowledge of how individuals work together (or don't!). Once experienced in small group work you can vary groups without too much fuss.
- Try random grouping or grouping according to things students have in common, e.g. food dislikes, favourite TV programmes, eye colours, etc.
- Keep groups together for about half a term to give time to gel – unless they just don't get on. This is particularly the case with base groups (see page 28).

Seating arrangements

- Use small circles, around the ends of benches or in the spaces between.
- Encourage students to move closer together to promote discussion and lower noise.
- Remember that the student in the most central position is likely to contribute most, and students side-by-side are less likely to communicate with the person sitting opposite.

Session flow

Students must get into the habit of working in their discussion groups so that they become routine and waste less time. Try planning and **rehearsing** these movements to develop this. Keeping groups together for several weeks will ease this process enormously.

Prior knowledge

- Preliminary presentation of background information before discussion avoids 'drying-up', poor debate and misbehaviour.
- Stimulus material is useful, e.g. videos, case studies, or information sheets. Previous work or experiments are also useful stimuli.
- Ensure the task is clearly understood.
- Set a time limit.
- Assign roles or tasks to group members or allow group to undertake this.
- Remind students of the importance of reporting back to the whole class, or the teacher. Effort is concentrated in this way.
- Reiterate the ground rules for group discussion, particularly in the early stages.

Appreciating view points

Students must learn to appreciate that their peers may have different opinions, which they hold equally strongly. A problem-solving task in which each student holds an important piece of information helps raise awareness of the need for understanding and cooperation. (All the pieces of information held by the students collectively solve the problem.) Once the problem has been completed, ask students:

- Could the solution have been found sooner? If so, how?
- Did students ignore information held by others? Were they wise to do this?
- Did anyone dominate?
- Did anyone not volunteer information?

Types of small groups

There are many different types of small discussion groups and each one is structured according to the group task. Five types we feel are the most useful in the classroom (and the most common) are described here.

Base groups

Carefully selected on the basis of friendship or compatibility, with a balance of academic and social skills, in order to:

- build long-term relationships and develop cooperative skills,
- foster coaching and collaboration, e.g. help one another with subject matter; checking homework; discussing ideas and problems; evaluating each other's work and progress; study groups for tests, etc.

Home groups

Short term groups with a regularly changing membership.
Commonly used to:

- plan or carry out specific tasks and activities,
- act as a forum for reporting back to the whole class.

Expert groups

Short term groups, usually formed by a representative from each home group. These groups have regularly changing membership. They:

- cooperatively research specific information to develop expertise on a particular aspect of the home group task,
- allow members to return to home groups to report their findings.

Informal or buzz-groups

Ad hoc groups formed to discuss or brainstorm ideas and suggestions, usually for only 5–10 minutes' duration.

Representative groups

Usually short term groups with changing membership; formed from, or used in conjunction with, any of the above groups. They can be assigned by the teacher or decided by each group. Representative groups meet apart from the class at any stage in the activity and are used:

- to provide a forum for whole class discussion or presentation,
- to give or receive information (or instructions) to and from other groups,
- to coordinate activities from the other groups,
- by the teacher to monitor progress or feed information to other groups,
- to help solve class problems,
- to carry out peer tutoring.

Relationship between group types

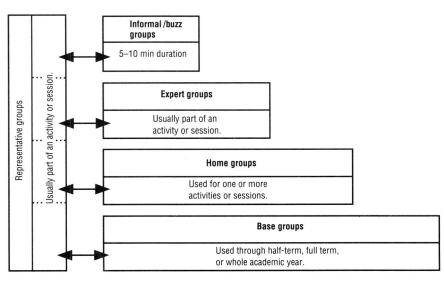

The jigsaw method – an example of group cooperative learning

The jigsaw method highlights the importance of small group discussion and collaborative learning. It is a useful technique for structuring the learning experience, and also spreading the workload at the same time. Jigsaw, as the name implies, requires each group member to take responsibility for researching and carrying out a particular piece of the overall task. Each group member then returns to their group in order to complete the group task.

The jigsaw method is best explained using the example in the student copymasters, Changes that affect animals and plants (see page 177). In this activity students are divided into home groups of four and given an agenda which poses a series of eight key questions on the seasonal changes affecting animals and plants. The groups are asked to discuss these for about ten minutes and share their initial thoughts. The teacher suggests that the best way to handle the task is to share responsibility for finding out specific information relating to the different areas covered by the questions. Each home group is subsequently split up, with members from each going to one of four expert groups.

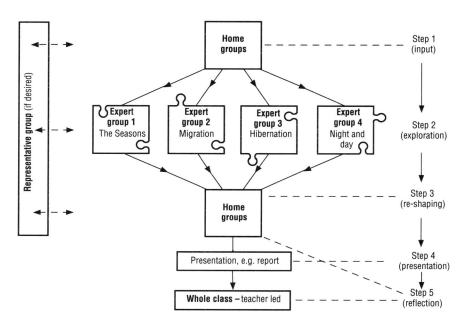

How the jigsaw method works.

The expert groups are each given a specific aspect of the questions to explore, i.e. one of the four information sheets. Approximately twenty minutes are allowed for this and groups are asked to record their discussions. Following this, the experts return to their home groups and share the knowledge they have gained. Students question one another to clarify, reorganise, and extend the information presented. They are now in a stronger position to discuss and answer the original questions. Students in their home groups can be asked to prepare a presentation of what they have learned. The teacher can ask students to reflect upon **what** and **how** they have learned. This helps the teacher to evaluate the learning and plan further development.

Although jigsaw may seem a rather complicated strategy it is much simpler in practice. Like all new strategies, teacher and student need to gain confidence in its use. Once short informal or step-by-step discussion sessions are perfected more adventurous strategies such as jigsaw can be introduced.

Progression through discussion strategies

Informal discussion (in pairs)	in steps →	Step-by-step discussion (in threes, fours)	in steps →	Jigsaw method (in fours, fives)	in steps →	Whole class discussion (everybody)
short duration, say 5 minutes	→	low interaction between groups; duration longer (approx.10 mins)	→	high interaction between small groups (approx. 1 hour)	→	whole class discussion; longer duration

Coping with student idiosyncracies

Silent or shy

- Place with friends.
- Allow preparation time to work out dialogue.
- Give time for confidence to build gradually.
- Introduce fixed time duration contributions from all students, in turn.
- Congratulate small contributions, but avoid over-attention.
- Invite comments directly, but be sensitive about this.
- Ban interruptions from other students.
- Take to one side and counsel if necessary.

Clown or distracter

- Confront; explain problems their behaviour causes.
- Give clear guidance on how behaviour should be improved.
- Reward better behaviour.
- Put into a group that is likely to discourage this behaviour.
- Separate from anyone who encourages this behaviour.
- Sit in with group at regular intervals.
- Exclude from discussion as last resort.

Apathetic or bored

- Place with friends.
- Encourage any sign of involvement.
- Give a specific role or task within the group.
- Try to make work as interesting and active as possible.
- Provide a variety of tasks and procedures.
- Allow student to choose topic, role or task.
- Make group membership optional and offer alternative work (as a last resort).
- Introduce an activity which requires a contribution from everyone.
- Take to one side and counsel if necessary.

Dominant or over talkative

- Share out time for making contributions.
- Allocate a role that involves recording or writing up.
- Provide feedback, perhaps using observer's checklist to show how dominant behaviour can be unfair to others. **However**, praise willingness to contribute.
- Suggest a leadership role so that individual can encourage others to participate.
- Place with similar students!

Duellists and aggressors

- Try to identify reasons for behaviour; talk through this and try to sort out difficulties.
- Point out the problems the behaviour causes others.
- Suggest preferred behaviour.
- Give advice on self-control and resolving conflict.
- Agree ground rules where aggression and arguing are not allowed.
- Separate known duellists.
- Exclude from discussion if necessary.

Sensitive issues

- Forewarn vulnerable students of discussion topic if possible and make participation optional.
- Provide alternative activities.
- Put vulnerable students in understanding group or one where the teacher is present.
- Consider avoiding highly sensitive topics.
- Agree ground rules which allow students to sit out if a topic is too sensitive.

31

Whole class discussion

Engaging a whole class in meaningful discussion is not easy. There are a number of inherent disadvantages:

Whole class discussion – some common problems:

- Teacher dominated
- Interactions mostly teacher to student
- Select number of students contribute or dominate
- Inhibits the shy or inarticulate
- Difficult to run effectively and sustain a controlled dialogue

So what strategies can we use to improve whole class discussion?

Managing a whole class discussion poses a considerable threat to both teacher and student. Most people feel much more at ease in a smaller group. Inhibitions and anxieties are amplified within a large group, making resistance, resentment and confrontation more difficult for the teacher to handle. Any attention seekers have a much larger audience to perform to.

The advice given on **active listening** together with the following strategies and techniques will help to bring stucture and control to the discussion. Some of the strategies have been used successfully for many years and in a wide range of groups, particularly in Personal and Social Education (PSE) programmes.

Many of the strategies discussed here can also be used in small group discussion.

ACTIVITY 3.5
Try a quick brainstorm by yourself or with a colleague on the next topic you are going to teach.

---

1 Brainstorming

Why use brainstorming?

- produces a lot of ideas quickly
- involves the whole class
- promotes imaginative and creative thinking
- pools ideas – twenty heads are better than one!
- It's fun, not threatening

Brainstorming is a useful strategy for the following:

- generating ideas; planning; reviewing; evaluating
- problem solving sessions
- planning practical work
- introducing a new topic
- revising a topic
- reviewing a video programme
- planning a visit or for a visitor
- drawing up an agenda for small group work
- evaluating activities
- summarising key points or issues

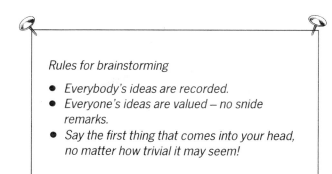

Teacher's notes

- Introduce topic and set a time limit.
- Ask for ideas; keep them flowing.
- Write down ideas in any order (throw in the odd one yourself).
- Record everything! It may stop them saying silly things.
- Value everyone's ideas equally.
- If ideas dry up don't take over – silence tells a group it's their responsibility.
- Discuss ideas and group them; encourage pupils to do this.

Don't forget – Break Duty

Rules for brainstorming

- *Everybody's ideas are recorded.*
- *Everyone's ideas are valued – no snide remarks.*
- *Say the first thing that comes into your head, no matter how trivial it may seem!*

2 The circle or rounds

The circle or rounds is a useful technique:

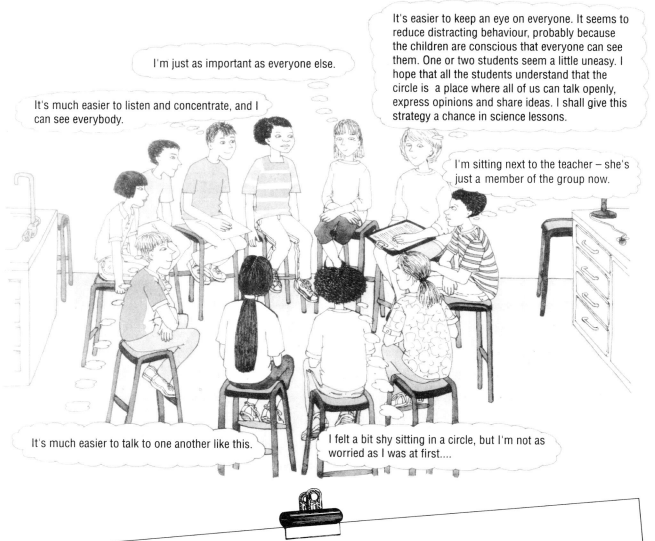

Rules for the circle or rounds

1 Everyone has a chance to comment on what is being discussed.
2 One student begins and the turn moves round the circle.
3 No one is allowed to comment on what anyone says, including the teacher.
4 Everyone has the right to say 'I pass' and refuse their turn.
5 If a comment is made which requires discussion it should be saved until after the rounds are completed.

Technique useful:

- whenever students are requested to express an opinion or give feedback – the circle is recognised as a safe place to speak, free from judgement or jibes,
- to discuss an experience e.g. a film, video, role play or simulation,
- to help activities or problem solving, e.g. 'I think we could try . . .',
- evaluation of activities, e.g. 'What I liked most about the practical was . . .'.

3 Nominal group technique (NGT)

Nominal group technique is useful for establishing group or class consensus without long, drawn out discussion. It is also useful for prioritising, e.g. agreeing the most suitable solution in problem-solving.

B

4 Other strategies

Probably the most common form of whole class discussion is the typical teacher exposition followed by a round of questions. This is a very limiting form of discussion and despite the fact that it is used regularly by science teachers it requires considerable skill to run effectively. If this form of discussion is used, try to bear the following in mind:

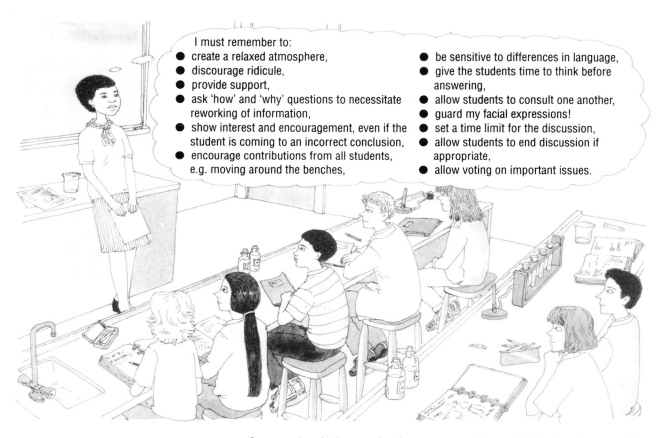

I must remember to:
- create a relaxed atmosphere,
- discourage ridicule,
- provide support,
- ask 'how' and 'why' questions to necessitate reworking of information,
- show interest and encouragement, even if the student is coming to an incorrect conclusion,
- encourage contributions from all students, e.g. moving around the benches,
- be sensitive to differences in language,
- give the students time to think before answering,
- allow students to consult one another,
- guard my facial expressions!
- set a time limit for the discussion,
- allow students to end discussion if appropriate,
- allow voting on important issues.

Games, simulations, role plays, case studies and debates also provide opportunities for whole class discussion, but these are explored in later chapters.

4

Active reading

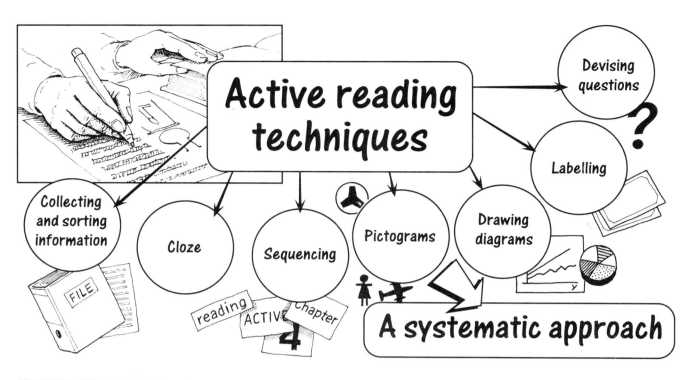

Introduction

Why encourage active reading?

Reading tends to be an activity which an eleven-year-old student is **expected** to perform. This is often just reinforced in secondary school with more demanding text. This creates the problem whereby students read without understanding. However, reading is an activity which must involve comprehension for it to be effective. The text needs to be deciphered. To assist comprehension the student needs to be actively involved.

What is the incidence of reading in science?

A reading survey* suggested that the incidence of reading in science was surprisingly low almost on a par with mathematics. The survey also reported that most reading activities usually lasted only 30 seconds:

Subject area	Incidence of reading	
	Year 7	*Year 10*
Science	9%	10%
Mathematics	10%	8%
Social studies	15%	16%

* Source: K. Gardner and E. A. Lunzer (Eds.) *Effective use of reading* (Heinemann Educational, for the Schools Council, 1979). This is the most recent, large-scale reading survey of this nature.

What forms of reading take place in science?

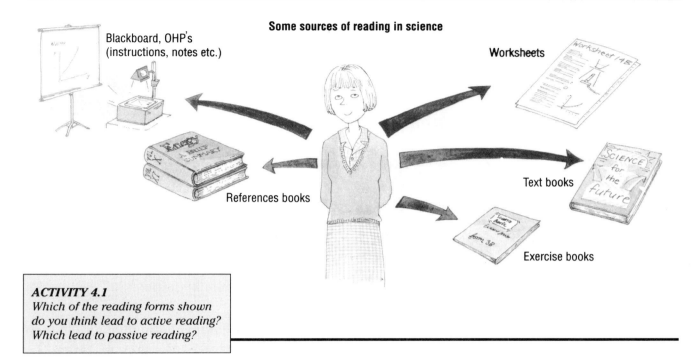

Some sources of reading in science

Blackboard, OHP's (instructions, notes etc.)

Worksheets

References books

Text books

Exercise books

ACTIVITY 4.1
Which of the reading forms shown do you think lead to active reading? Which lead to passive reading?

The answer to the previous activity is, of course, all forms are active – **if** appropriately conducted. Reading from the blackboard is very passive if the teacher simply expects students to copy work. Blackboards are used more actively if they are employed to display brainstorms or headings and unfamiliar terms. Essentially, students must have some active control over the process.

Textbooks and reference books are often used in passive homework activities. Students are frequently asked to read a chapter purely to make notes on a topic for a test on Monday, or to answer questions on page 176. Often, this is only a study in plagiarism! Without detailed guidance most students achieve very little in a reading activity. Some students **are** capable of making their own notes and gleaning useful information, but often the reading age of the text is too high and user-unfriendly. Ultimately, students should be actively involved in seeking information because of a personal need to find out, not as a response to imposed constraints. The latter only reduces motivation and effective learning.

Many worksheets also receive a passive response. This is especially true when they consist solely of instructions. Again, the text is determining the reading purpose.

You've read the book

You've made the notes

QUIET EXAM

What was it all about?

$F = ma$ plus one headache!

What makes an active reader?

Active readers:

- see underlying ideas through the text,
- compare ideas with what they already know,
- pick out what is essential and new,
- revise preconceptions accordingly,

The key to effective reading is the reader's ability to make connections between what is being read and his or her existing knowledge or ideas.

Using the strategy

Comparison of active reading and science practical work

The active processes encouraged by active reading are directly analogous to the ordered processes used all the time during practical investigations. The diagram reflects this correlation.

Practical investigation   **Active reading process**

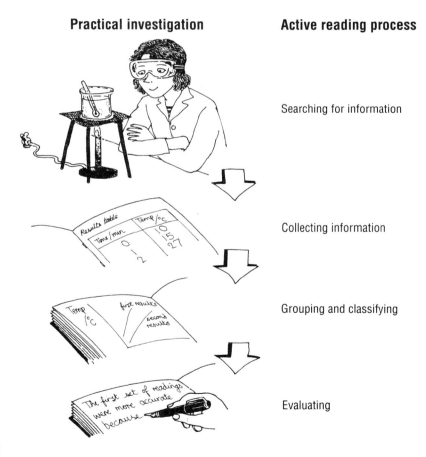

Searching for information

Collecting information

Grouping and classifying

Evaluating

ACTIVITY 4.2
Collect examples of DARTS together from your own teaching experience and list the methods used in them to encourage active reading.

Objectives in practical work need to be clear and the teacher can act as a guide. Similarly, in order to focus the students' attention to reading, direction is needed. There are numerous ways in which Directed Activities Related to Text (DARTS) are achieved.

Collecting and sorting information

Library searches to find out specific information for project work can be made more active if the information is classified or sorted in some way. Pre-selected passages of text can be used to limit the degree of initial research necessary.

Cloze

Cloze is a predicting exercise. Words are deleted from a text at intervals, e.g. every fifth, every tenth word, etc. Students are then asked to reconstruct the text by predicting the missing words.

e.g. Digestion is the process _____ which insoluble food, consisting _____ large molecules, is broken _____ into soluble compounds having _____ molecules.

Deletion on an irregular basis offers even greater potential:
e.g. Digestion is the process by which insoluble food, consisting of _____ molecules, is broken down into _____ compounds having smaller molecules.

With irregular deletion the teacher has control over the word omitted, and can choose important or key words to leave out. Cloze works best when the initial few lines have no deletions at all, since it helps students to follow the text style. A final paragraph without deletions is also useful.

Cloze can be used:

- as a basic study skill,
- to assess a pupil's understanding of a topic,
- to involve students in decision making,
- to increase motivation,
- to stimulate group discussion.

If cloze is used, guard against the following:

- it needs to be used selectively,
- it can produce unpredictable responses,
- deletions need to be carefully considered,
- too many deletions are frustrating,
- the technique makes no attempt to analyse text if deletions are regular.

ACTIVITY 4.3
Create your own cloze and trial it with a class.

Sequencing

This is a powerful technique closely allied to the cloze method. In sequencing the text is physically divided up and then shuffled. Students must rearrange the pieces of text into the correct order. Sequencing can also be done with the aid of diagrams. If a cyclical process is chosen for sequencing, e.g. the water cycle, the shuffled pieces of information can be correctly ordered by the student on to a diagram which illustrates the process. Other examples that can be used to illustrate this are the nitrogen and carbon cycles. An example of this can be seen in Birkett, I. and Walker, A. (1990, activity 19).

Sequencing is particularly useful for developing planning skills for practicals. Practical instructions can be muddled and given to a student, who must then put them into the correct order. The exercise can be made more difficult by omitting some instructions.

Sequencing can be used:

- to encourage active reading,
- to encourage students to focus on the experimental purpose,
- to make students consider the logical order of events,
- to build on experimental planning and design skills,
- to encourage group discussion.

However:

- segments need to be linked and have natural breaks.

ACTIVITY 4.4
Draw up a list of instructions for your next class experiment. Cut these into sections and try the sequencing technique with a class.

Pictograms

Pictograms are similar in essence to the exercises found in children's puzzle books where a word is changed into a picture. Whilst the transmission of knowledge in pictograms is quite low they are fun to do and can motivate students, especially younger ones. They may also aid memory. A brief example is given here:

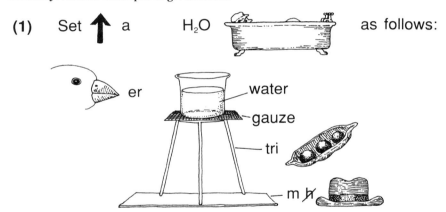

Emphasis

This technique can be used to pick out single words, phrases, sentences, paragraphs or data from a text. Emphasising helps with revision and the general organisation of work. Try encouraging students to:

- emphasise key words or concepts,
- classify work using colour coding, underlining, highlighting or ringing,
- highlight areas of text according to purpose, e.g. statement of fact, opinion, application of idea, etc.

ACTIVITY 4.5
Think about a text you use often with students. Try an underlining technique with it and see if students read the passage more actively.

For a fuller treatment of these ideas see chapter 2, Study skills. An example of an emphasising activity is given in the student copymaster, Nuclear reactor, on page 186.

Drawing diagrams

In many situations teachers use diagrams of apparatus or flow diagrams of experimental stages to aid students' understanding. It is also important to get students using the same technique, for their own benefit. Some students are averse to using symbolic representation, and the solution is to reverse the process. The approach is easy to introduce. Try photocopying an experimental account from a student's notebook. Distribute copies to other members of the group or class, and get them to produce a title for the written piece, and a drawing of the main apparatus.

Alternatively, use the student copymaster, Coal, on page 188. In this activity, students are asked to complete a diagram by reading a passage of text.

Diagram and flow chart construction is useful because:

- it helps students visualise,
- it aids revision, and note-taking,
- students consider the logical order of events.

But remember:

- students may have problems with scale,
- students are hindered by concerns about neatness,
- students are sometimes reluctant to finalise draft copies.

Labelling

The labelling of diagrams can be used to encourage actively reading for information. To begin with, labels can be supplied for cutting out and sticking on to prepared diagrams. Students can progress from this to examining text to find appropriate labels for diagrams.

This technique can be used:

- to encourage students to ask questions about text,
- to get students to consider ideas hidden in text,
- to annotate diagrams as an *aide-mémoire*,
- to help students classify text.

But remember:

- careful selection of diagrams and text is important,
- too many labels may cause confusion.

Devising questions

The approach used here is somewhat a reverse comprehension exercise, whereby groups of students are given a text and asked to construct questions on salient points. Groups then exchange questions, answer them and hand them back for marking. This promotes considerable debate!

This technique can be used:

- to ascertain what questions cause students problems (students often generate questions with which they would have difficulty),
- to increase motivation – students enjoy writing their own questions for a change,
- to identify confusion in text,
- to act as an introduction to a topic.

But remember:

- Students often like to access secondary sources of information and go beyond the text to make questions more difficult,
- the text itself needs to be readily accessible.

A systematic approach to active reading

There are many models for a systematic approach to active reading. The basic elements common to each of them are described in the flow chart:

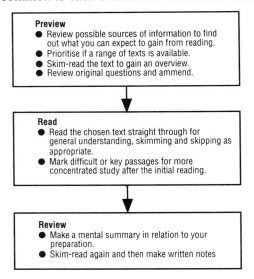

The combination of this kind of systematic study reading combined with small group discussion (in the preparation, preview, and review stages) is very powerful, especially when students have begun to develop these skills and approaches.

Active reading in the National Curriculum for Science — an integrated approach

ACTIVITY 4.6
Try a DARTS approach to the remaining text in this chapter.
(a) Underline key points.
(b) Design a flow chart linking the progression of ideas in the text with the requirements of the communication element National Curriculum for Science programmes of study (key stages 3 and 4). (We hope this emphasises the benefit of using a DARTS technique when tackling difficult ideas through text!)

The relation between the model for systematic active reading and the exploration of science statements in the National Curriculum is interesting. Not only do the statements make regular and specific reference to the need for literature searches and the use of secondary sources, but the systematic approach to investigation presented in the statements echoes the systematic approach to reading, particularly in the preparation stage. These two approaches are mutually supportive.

The National Curriculum also stresses the importance of communicating the results of an investigation. An important stimulus to active reading is a genuine and personally-perceived need on the part of the student to find something out by reading. This requirement will usually be met by the student making genuine and worthwhile use of the results of his or her reading, often by communicating them to others in some way.

An equally important factor in stimulating the development of active reading skills is the confidence, born of students' previous successful experience, that they will be able to find out what they **want** to know, through reading. This is an essential factor in developing the students' disposition to reading for information. It has significant implications for resourcing both in science departments and in school libraries. The most useful texts for this purpose are those which present information in a readable, and clearly organised fashion, including an index. This way students become increasingly independent at finding information within a book, a range of books, or a library. The least useful texts are those in which information is closely interwoven with a sequential format of exercises.

The programmes of study for key stages 3 and 4 present an important sense of progression in reading skills.

Programme of study, key stage 3

Communication 'They should be encouraged to read purposefully an extended range of secondary sources. They should take increasing responsibility for selecting resources.'

Programme of study, key stage 4

Communication 'They should develop research skills through selecting and using reference materials and through gathering and organising information from a number of sources and perspectives. They should have opportunities to translate information from one form to another to suit audience and purpose.'

During these stages, students should be gradually and systematically introduced to the study reading model described in this book, so that they become confident, flexible, and efficient in their use of reading skills. Initially, students should be supported, e.g. with preparation frameworks, or participation in teacher-led reading activities. An important skill which can be developed this way is an awareness of the organisation of text. Students learn to recognise distinct sections such as introductory pieces, concluding summaries and exemplars.

Students must become increasingly independent with reading. A too prolonged diet of teacher-directed reading is likely to produce students who are reliant on teachers for motivation and see personal study as something which is externally imposed. Consequently, these students tend not to make connections, and seek only the 'right' answer. They find it difficult to accept a variety of opinions. The active reading techniques described in this chapter will help to prevent this.

The nature of science element of the National Curriculum provides an interesting vehicle for the development of active reading skills. Students, either individually or in groups, can consider topics that interest them and the scientific advances which have led to the present state of that topic. In the early stages of the development of this approach, it is important that students are involved with topics with which they have some familiarity. This facilitates the framing of preparatory questions and makes connections through the reading process easier. A period of active study reading should follow, possibly culminating in a modern museum-type exhibit featuring a working model, graphics, text panels, guide-book entry or audio tape commentary. This type of project can usefully double as a National Curriculum technology project.

5

Active writing

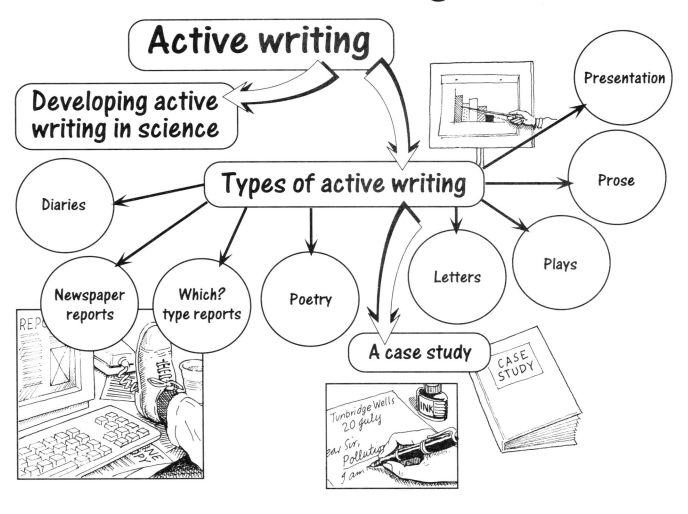

Active writing

Developing active writing in science

Types of active writing

- Diaries
- Newspaper reports
- Which? type reports
- Poetry
- A case study
- Letters
- Plays
- Prose
- Presentation

Introduction

Why encourage active writing?

Active writing teaches students to:

- *take responsibility for their own writing,*
- *clarify and express their own ideas,*
- *communicate their findings to others,*
- *express personal feelings and reactions to scientific issues and theories.*

Work which involves methodical copying from the blackboard or a textbook is not conducive to effective learning, since the act of writing is passive and does not necessarily involve the student in thought. Second, not all students enjoy the formal write-ups demanded by science teachers, particularly when writing up investigations. Active writing needs to be fostered in which students are asked to clarify and order scientific ideas and information for a real purpose – and in their own words.

The writing can allow students to express their ideas about phenomena and experiences. To enable this the teacher can carefully plan lessons to incorporate a variety of learning approaches which will motivate and engage student interest.

Teaching which offers a choice and variety in writing styles can support scholarship in other curriculum areas, and will appeal to the students' preferred learning styles. For some students in year 7 it may well be possible to build on recent primary science experience, in which they might have already written for a variety of purposes and audiences.

How does active writing fit in with the National Curriculum for science?

Increasingly, school science textbooks are encouraging teachers to provide opportunities for students to write actively. The programmes of study for communication (key stages 3 and 4) stress the need for active writing: students 'should be encouraged to express their ideas and to respond to those of others' (key stage 3); students 'should be given opportunities to develop their skills of reporting and recording'; 'They should have opportunities to translate information from one form to another to suit audience and purpose' (key stage 4, Double Science).

Using the strategy

What types of active writing can be used?

Active and creative writing include:

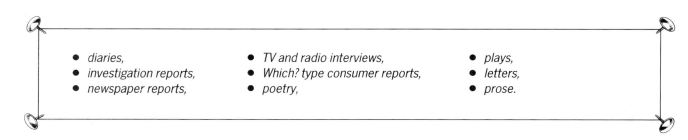

- diaries,
- investigation reports,
- newspaper reports,

- TV and radio interviews,
- Which? type consumer reports,
- poetry,

- plays,
- letters,
- prose.

These writing approaches help students to clarify their own thinking in science, just as small group discussion allows students to explore ideas.

How can active writing approaches be developed in science lessons?

Oh, not newspaper articles again...I didn't come to school just to learn how to be a journalist..

Initially, science teachers need to recognise the value of providing students with a variety of writing experiences. Discussion with colleagues in the English department can be helpful. A school-wide curriculum focus for developing language for learning is particularly beneficial. Senior management need to be involved in an initiative of this type to structure meetings between all departments. It must be made clear that they are not working in isolation but towards a school policy on producing literate, thinking students. A review of the writing experiences provided by each department will reveal any gaps in the students' writing entitlement. Quantification of the time spent on each writing category, each year, will reveal if the coverage is balanced enough both in each department and across the school. If students find themselves doing newspaper reports in several areas of the curriculum it will have a de-motivating effect. To assist a more varied writing approach teachers need to try different writing styles, evaluate their effect, and share their experiences with other colleagues in the department (or across the school). Contractual obligations to try new approaches with reporting back can be an effective way of managing the introduction of a new pedagogy.

Existing teaching resources

An increasing number of references to creative writing materials are made in science curriculum publications. SSCR (Sheffield Working Group), *Biotech* (ASE, 1987) uses biotechnology as a vehicle to develop a variety of teaching and learning approaches in science, a few of which make use of active writing. Some suitable published examples of this type of material are mentioned in this chapter.

Active writing techniques

Diaries

Diaries are an excellent way of enhancing a student's written scientific account. The approach allows students to communicate difficulties in a non-public way. However, for this approach to be useful the teacher has to be prepared to **read** the diaries and **respond** to them effectively. A red tick is not enough – written feedback from the teacher is critical.

Diaries:

- *give students the opportunity to reflect on their own learning (an important link to records of achievement and experience),*
- *allow students to communicate their own ideas on a topic before any teaching begins. This idea has been developed by the Children's Learning in Science Project (CLIS),*

- *give teachers valuable insight into student understanding, particularly useful in mixed ability classes,*
- *provide writing opportunities for **real communication** and allow students to clarify and record information.*

That many!
That's almost 50 cigarettes a week!

Diaries have been used in health education to help students reflect on their own behaviour and consider health implications for the future. A 2-week diary of a student's (or peer, family member, etc.) behaviour towards his/her own dental hygiene, smoking, drinking, and eating habits provides valuable information with which to contemplate long term effects of personal habits. The diary forms an important mechanism for developing the skill of **critical reflection**.

Science 'think books' are another useful active writing tool. SSCR (Wiltshire) *Science think books: an introduction to their use in science lessons* (ASE, 1987) is a useful introduction to the purpose of think books. The books are intended to help students review and plan ahead for certain learning journeys. Students can write freely on:

- what they already know,
- what they are unsure of,
- the contribution they may need from the teacher,
- how they feel about their work and their achievement in science (record of achievement and experience).

Science think books are essentially a special type of diary. The student views it as a journal in which to raise questions and express concerns to the teacher. It is quoted in the SSCR (Wiltshire), *Science think books*: 'the way the teacher answers the questions is good but I think some questions cannot be answered because may be the teacher does not know the answer

ACTIVITY 5.1
Jot down your ideas on the written feedback you anticipate students will find supportive in their diaries. What sort of feedback might prove unhelpful?

but guesses or some cannot be answered in words but in action'. This approach supports the work of CLIS since it encourages teachers to establish what existing ideas students have and plan learning programmes accordingly.

Newspaper reports

Newspapers are part of the world in which students live. The medium is relevant to students and should be used to provide opportunities to write for different audiences.

'The Biotech Bugle' (Unit 2, Yeast Technology Today) in SSCR (Sheffield working group), *Biotech* contains an example of the use of newspapers to communicate scientific developments. This presents in an amusing way that in other cultures biotechnology provides an alternative source of energy for cars. To accompany this, a set of slides (available from the ASE) is shown to students illustrating the fermenter at Bassetts' sweet factory. Students are told to imagine that they are journalists on a tour of the factory and that they will have to produce a written report for either the local evening newspaper or a local radio station. The purpose of the exercise is made explicit in this way and students have a reason to watch the slides. The actual writing of the article gives them freedom to communicate the technology, its importance to the company, and their feelings on the potential benefits of the discovery to both local and national communities. Word processing facilities can be used to simulate work usually done by local journalists, the end product provides an interesting display for the school. Alternatively students could present their ideas in the form of a cartoon or comic strip. This is useful for communicating ideas to students in primary feeder schools. Once again, this encourages students to write for a real purpose.

ACTIVITY 5.2
List a range of topics that might encourage students to create newspaper reports.

In S. Beer, D. Edwards, R. Jackson, *Thinking through science: activities from chemistry 1*, D. Edwards (Ed.) (Collins Educational, 1989), pp. 28–9 there are opportunities for students to imagine they are journalists. Students are presented with information on the use of alcool (alcohol made from sugar) in Brazil as an alternative to petrol for cars. They are invited to write an article for a newspaper, drawing from the page content. Students are asked to explain the benefits of the fuel for the people of Brazil, and how scientists have developed it.

The use of newspaper articles to communicate scientific facts and issues is becoming increasingly common in response to the National Curriculum for science and its emphasis on the communication of scientific ideas.

Comics frequently form the reading stage prior to adult newspapers. Constructing a cartoon strip to communicate an aspect of scientific work can also be used to foster active writing. Comic strips are perhaps more creative since they incorporate drawings as well. The process involves mental interaction with ideas as students think about how to communicate them.

Cartoon strips are used in T. Smith, C. Tear, A. Yate, *Thinking through science: activities from physics 1*, D. Edwards (Ed.) (Collins Educational, 1989), pp.14–15 and M. Coles, R. Gott, T. Thornley, *Active Science 2* (Collins Educational, 1989), p. 94, to present ideas to students on forces and salt, respectively.

Which? type consumer reports

Which? type investigations allowing students to practise the manipulation of independent and dependent variables are becoming more common in the science curriculum. SSCR (Sheffield working group), *Biotech* conducts a *Which?* type consumer investigation on the manufacturers' claims about biological washing powders in the unit called 'Washday biotech'. The communication aspect of the investigation is an important part of the process and rather than producing a formal write-up, students are asked to compile a report on behalf of the Consumer Advice Service. Students are told that their job is to test products such as washing powders, and are asked to write a straightforward leaflet for the public telling them what they have found out. The production of an attractive and interesting leaflet also gives students the chance to develop design skills.

In I. Olejnk, *Biology in daily life* (Blackie, 1988), p. 59, the potential of balanite trees in protecting farmland from the world's expanding deserts is explained. The learning strategy suggested is for the reader to imagine s/he is a United Nations agricultural representative in one of the countries of the Sahel. The student must design and prepare a fact sheet to tell people why they should plant balanite trees. The reader is also asked which medium they would use to convey the information to farmers in these areas (posters? TV? presentations?). This again provides real information for students but allows them to use it to develop their understanding in a creative way, whilst communicating to others.

M. Coles, R. Gott, T. Thornley, *Active Science 2*, p. 85 also develops Which? type investigations in a unit on alkalis. Students are asked to investigate which indigestion powder is best at neutralising stomach acids. Although the investigation does not encourage an active form of write-up, the opportunity is clearly there.

> **ACTIVITY 5.3**
> *Choose an attainment target from the National Curriculum for science and look for topics which will lend themselves to the consumer report approach.*

Poetry

K. Johnston, 'CLIS news 2' (CLIS, 1987) states 'with a little imagination we can perhaps give our students a powerful tool to assist them in making sense of the science.' The National Writing Project also suggests that there is more to writing than the formal stuff of exercise books.

Poetry has rarely been emphasised in the secondary science curriculum. If we pause to consider why people write poetry (or music for that matter) it is usually based on experiences or feelings which have had a significant effect upon the writer. If poetry is seen as a student vehicle to express their views it is serving a learning purpose analogous to keeping diaries or journals. Poetry is a medium which some students like to use and which teachers can offer occasionally.

The National Curriculum for science requires students to consider human influences on the earth. The programmes of study say that students should consider current concerns about human activity, including the exploitation of resources, the disposal of waste products on the Earth, in its oceans and atmosphere, and the effects on climate. Poetry is a suitable medium for students to express their feelings on such issues. The poems can reach a wider audience if the school has its own magazine.

The following poem 'Beginning' illustrates the potential of poetry as a learning tool in science:

> At the beginning
> You were not there.
> Nothing of you, but an egg cell.
> Just waiting for the sperm to appear.
> Suddenly there's a jolt of movement
> And it appears
> It comes towards you and you clash together
> The sperm didn't have to push hard
> to get in

The ovum was soft
Now they were joined as one cell
Belonging together
Then split into two, four and eight
You grow and grow
You move towards the womb
Your mum's womb changes
So you can grow safely
You start to form a head
What is supposed to be a head
Not much of a baby yet.

(Poem supplied by year 7, Gleadless School, Sheffield.)

Letters

> *Writing letters in science:*
>
> - *aids revision,*
> - *develops and reinforces concepts,*
> - *helps teachers to identify things students have misunderstood,*
> - *introduces a style of science writing that is useful in later life.*

Writing letters at the end of a module, unit or topic provides students with a context for communicating what they have learned. ASE, *Language in science*, study series no. 16, (ASE, 1980), p. 68 includes a letter used for this purpose. Paula, a 14-year-old student completed a unit on the eye. She observed the eye in action, dissected a bull's eye, and constructed a labelled diagram. Paula was asked by her teacher to write a letter to a friend explaining the function of the eye:

Dear Caroline,

I am writing in reply to your enquiry as to how the eye works. First of all imagine it is like a camera with the workings showing. As the light passes through the lens of the camera and leaves an imprint of the object on the film so the eye works in the same way. The light passing through the pupil and leaving an imprint on the retina. The imprint being upside down, it now passes along the optic nerve to the brain where it is processed and made to look the right way up. The iris controls the amount of light going into the eye and the pupil contracts when the light is bright and expands when the light is dull. The yellow spot is in line with the centre of the lens. It has no nerves over the sense cells so light falling on this part of the retina makes a very clear picture.

Yours faithfully,

Paula

Teacher's comment – 'I know the explanation of the image and its transference to the brain is unsophisticated but at this level I consider this a very clear description.' Paula has also demonstrated that she can communicate her knowledge to a friend.

Letter writing also encourages students to raise questions and seek solutions. Students can be encouraged to write questions to the agony columns of magazines (e.g. on health education issues) or write their own enquiry letters. Follow-up research can be done on the answers they receive.

'Problem' letters could be written by half a school-class and sent to the other half for replies. This type of work is informative and enjoyable, too.

Letter writing also prepares students for citizenship. Students will undoubtedly have to write letters during their adult life. An excellent introduction to official letter-writing is environmental work. Quantitative surveys of the amount of litter in the school neighbourhood can lead to student correspondence with local officials. If litter is caused by overflowing bins, students can arm themselves with the necessary information to write letters to governors, councillors, environmental health officers, etc. Student motivation is high, out of a need to change very real problems.

ACTIVITY 5.4
Look for other scientific issues which will stimulate group discussion followed by letter writing.

Biological powder, or non-biological powder – that is the question...

ACTIVITY 5.5
Writing a short playlet helps students gain insight into scientific ideas. Brainstorm some ideas for playlets in science.

Plays

Children throughout the whole secondary age range enjoy reading plays. School trials of 'The insulin story' in SSCR (Sheffield working group), *Biotech*, have been immensely successful. The story is a drama/play which conveys to students the history of diabetes from ancient to modern times, including a consideration of the benefits of genetically engineered insulin.

The play can be linked to an activity which encourages students to reflect on each act by summarising the symptoms, treatment and future of a patient who becomes ill with diabetes at different periods of history, from ancient Egyptian times to the present day. Reflectively structuring a summary can provide a basis for more extended writing at the end of the activity. The play challenges students to think about what it was like to live in those days before the discovery of modern vaccinations. This very real situation also urges students to analyse the cause of the disease. Play reading provides a stimulus for role play or structured discussion.

There is no reason why plays should not be written by the students themselves and shared with the rest of the class. Many scientific and technological impacts on society lend themselves to the consideration of issues. Exploring issues, via play writing, to which there are no right or wrong answers, actively involves children in these issues. Both the writer and reader are encouraged to make personal judgements about what is best for society, e.g. whether biological washing powders save electrical energy.

Short plays containing brief scenes for a simulated TV advert provide another way for students to explore ideas before presenting them to others. In this way, students can creatively set about something which is not directly related to a laboratory situation but is still scientific.

Prose

Prose writing is becoming increasingly common in science textbooks. The Children's Learning in Science project encourages prose writing for tracing the development of students' existing ideas of scientific concepts. The theory of the particulate nature of matter is not easy for young scientists to assimilate. However, students could start to use this theory by studying the distillation of two liquids. Rather than get students to produce a formal write-up ask them to imagine they are a particle of water, and describe what happens to them during the separation process. This technique is analogous to pieces of prose students may have written at primary school. The accounts are often more enjoyable to read and give more insight into the thinking behind the work. Students have to interact mentally with ideas and language in a creative way to produde an experimental report.

Active prose writing is being incorporated into new science curriculum materials. For example, in M. Coles, R. Gott, T. Thornley, *Active Science 1* (Collins Educational, 1988), p. 125, there is a unit on electricity, which describes the concept of voltage, and illustrates graphically how lightning is produced. At the end of the unit, students are asked to draw on this knowledge, and then explain to a friend how lightning happens. In R. Gott, G. Price, T. Thornley, *Active Science 3* (Collins Educational, 1991), pp. 20–21, the causes of folding and faulting in rock structures are examined. The story of how Ingleborough Hill, Yorkshire formed, is then studied, with the aid of diagrams. Students are asked to use the information given to write a story on how the present landscape was formed.

> **ACTIVITY 5.6**
> *Write down a list of science topics which might provide an opportunity for creative prose writing.*

Presentation

The presentation of reports on group experiments to the rest of the class can provide valuable active writing experience. Posters, leaflets and overhead transparencies can be made to communicate ideas to others. This aspect of active writing is dealt with in greater detail in chapter 6, Presentation.

Displaying

Examples of active writing can produce a stimulating display for the science department, or indeed the whole school. Students can share responsibility for preparing and mounting displays, which will help to promote their own self-esteem and contribute to the school-ethos.

The case history at the end of this chapter illustrates the potential that exists, within the context of learning in science, to explore and develop a student's ability to write actively.

What are the possible problems?

The following comments point out shortfalls in active writing exercises which should be guarded against:

- 'I don't know what to put'
- 'Why are we writing like this?'
- 'This is a waste of time'
- 'Not newspapers again'
- 'I don't want people to look at my diary'

To counteract this the teacher can:

- provide a range or activities,
- keep initial active writing projects short,
- encourage group discussion of activities to provide ownership,
- liaise with other departments,
- in the case of diaries ensure privacy.

An example of using active writing

The example which follows is based on an attempt to encourage lower secondary students to write creatively in science.

During the introduction of the National Curriculum for science (key stage 3) a department developed a unit called 'Small things', in which students studied microbes. To explore the nature of science simultaneously with knowledge and content some of the work by the nineteenth-century scientist Dr John Snow was included. Dr Snow's efforts at eliminating a serious cholera epidemic in London, in 1848, formed the basis of this work unit.

Several textbooks provide information on this particular case study including M. Coles, R. Gott, T. Thornley, *Active Science 2*, p. 25. Independent Television made a schools broadcast on this, called *One man's sewerage*, presented by David Bellamy.

Rather than tell students the history of this event in a didactic way, students can watch a presentation of the event on television. This will focus the activity on the scientific processes which John Snow used to establish the cause of cholera, and provide a basis for paired discussion on the hypotheses, predictions, observations, recording methods, interpretations, conclusions, and recommendations identified by Dr Snow for eliminating the epidemic. The television presentation also allows students to gain visual insight into the living conditions of nineteenth-century Broad Street. Further small group discussion will enable students to share their perceptions and ideas on how Dr Snow solved the problem, and what it must have been like to live through such an epidemic. Students can then be given a choice of activities:

- Students imagine they are a newspaper reporter working for 'The Broad Street Chronicle'. Students write two articles – one reporting the beginning of the cholera outbreak, and one after Dr Snow had closed down the Broad Street pump. A crossword can be designed for the readers, in which the questions give clues to the scientific processes which Dr Snow used in preventing further cholera. A word processor (or DTP system) could be used to write a 'frontpage-extra' more actively.
- Students imagine they are a person who survives the cholera outbreak, and write a diary of their experience. This can be done in the format of a real diary.

- Students imagine they are a young person living in Broad Street in 1848, and write a letter describing the epidemic to a cousin who lives outside London.
- A small group of students write a play to convey what happened and what it was like to live through the epidemic. Imaginary characters can be created to complement real ones. The opportunity to reinforce (or refine) ideas prior to (or during) collaborative writing, can be taken by students. Ideas can be discussed in the non-threatening environment of small groups.
- Social-scientific history of this nature also provides students with the chance to express scientific feelings through poetry.

ACTIVITY 5.7
Brainstorm, if possible with another colleague, other suitable topics for active writing techniques, similar to those identified in the cholera epidemic case study.

6

Presentation

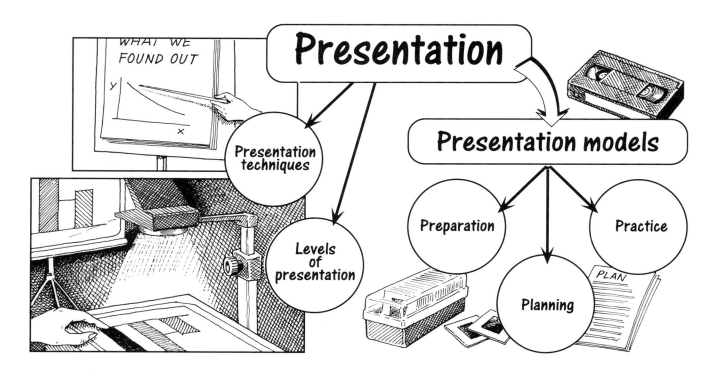

Introduction

Why are presentation skills important?

The ability to communicate ideas in a clear and interesting way is a great asset. In adult life presentations may be required at work, or due to a social commitment. In either situation self-confidence born of training and practice is invaluable. In school, students are increasingly asked to report on school work by means other than writing.

What do we mean by presentation?

We define a presentation as any situation in which students, or groups of students, are required to present information or discuss issues in front of an audience. The audience can be a small group, a whole class, or an adult audience.

Are effective presenters born or made?

Some people are naturally gifted at standing in front of an audience and, without any apparent effort, being entertaining and informative. It is not the aim of this chapter to emulate these role models. However, with a structured approach to presentation, and some practice, students can dramatically improve their presentation skills.

Are there some golden rules for giving presentations?

Yes – Read on!

Using the strategy

Presentation technique

How often have you had these thoughts while sitting through a lecture or talk?

ACTIVITY 6.1
Brainstorm the characteristics of the type of speaker who inspires you to present better.

You may have listed some of the following characteristics: clearly spoken, confident, well organised, well prepared, interesting, to-the-point, etc. The duration of a talk is also important. It is these very factors that are very off-putting to many students. Speaking in front of an audience is very frightening for young people, and it is important that students are not put off by their first experience of presentation. The following advice should help to minimise this risk:

Introducing presentation technique

- Allow students to present a topic that is familiar to them and one they feel comfortable with.
- Keep initial presentations very short.
- Arrange small audiences, e.g. use small group work.
- Allow time to rehearse presentations.
- Consider allowing presentations by groups. (The 'safety-in-numbers' mentality is helpful.)
- Allow the audience to ask a few questions of the speakers. (Students often unbend, and show greater depth of knowledge.)

Levels of presentation

The level of presentation depends on three factors: the complexity of the presentation, the size of the audience and the formality of the occasion. All forms of presentation fit within this framework, and recognising exactly where will assist constructive planning. The sort of presentation required for a brief report back to a small group is often not equally applicable for a presentation to a full assembly in the main hall!

The model shows the three factors as segments of a circle. The closer one moves towards the centre of the circle the more challenging a presentation will be. It seems sensible to introduce presentation skills by tackling examples in the outer regions of the circle and then moving in towards the centre as experience and confidence grows. It is worth noting, however, that the ultimate aim of this chapter is not to master long, complex presentations in front of large audiences, to the exclusion of all other types of presentation. All presentations are valid, but it is the more complex ones which demand carefully practised skills. Small-scale, low-threat examples are the surest way of doing this.

Presentation level

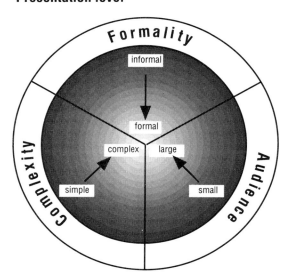

The presentation model

The successful use of preparations can be split into three stages: preparation, planning and practice.

Preparation

Preparation is vital. This initial stage can be sub-divided into a series of questions. It is a good idea to introduce students to these questions, possibly as a checklist. Maximum value is obtained from the process if pupils actively draw up their own list to compare with yours.

ACTIVITY 6.2
Before reading any further, try to formulate your own preparation checklist.

Preparation checklist

The following questions need to be considered. We have broadly classified them as follows:

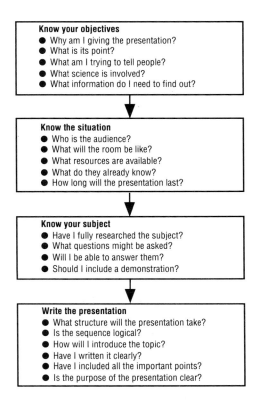

Know your objectives
● Why am I giving the presentation?
● What is its point?
● What am I trying to tell people?
● What science is involved?
● What information do I need to find out?

Know the situation
● Who is the audience?
● What will the room be like?
● What resources are available?
● What do they already know?
● How long will the presentation last?

Know your subject
● Have I fully researched the subject?
● What questions might be asked?
● Will I be able to answer them?
● Should I include a demonstration?

Write the presentation
● What structure will the presentation take?
● Is the sequence logical?
● How will I introduce the topic?
● Have I written it clearly?
● Have I included all the important points?
● Is the purpose of the presentation clear?

Planning

This stage can also be tackled by working through a checklist of questions:

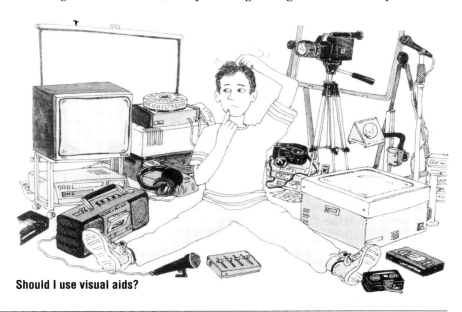

Should I use visual aids?

● Where will I gather the information?
● Do I need notes, a script or memory cards?
● Do I need to prepare worksheets, posters, or overhead transparencies before the presentation?
● Is it varied and interesting?
● Should I use visual aids:
  – What is available?
  – Is it easy to use?
  – Is it going to improve understanding of the presentation?
  – What will I do if the visual aid fails during the presentation?
● Is a group presentation suitable?
● How will the work be arranged? Should we split up and each do a section?
● How will we decide who does what?
● How will we ensure everyone does their fair share?

Practice

Students should be encouraged to rehearse their presentations. Instruct students to read through presentations aloud, and at least three times. This ensures:

- familiarity with the material,
- students feel confident and sound confident.
- students can coordinate the use of visual aids whilst talking,
- the presentation is completed in the planned time.

In order to allow practise it is important to provide sufficient time and space. The latter should, where possible, be away from other students. This reduces disruption to the group as a whole, and lowers the level of theat to people practising a presentation. Give presenters a tape recorder if one is available so that they can replay their efforts for evaluation. Warn them that most people sound strange on tape!

Golden rules and hints

Students should bear the following in mind when doing a presentation. Tell students they form part of a checklist of what teachers look for in a presentation.

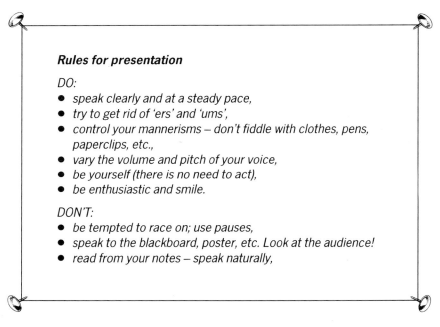

Rules for presentation

DO:
- *speak clearly and at a steady pace,*
- *try to get rid of 'ers' and 'ums',*
- *control your mannerisms – don't fiddle with clothes, pens, paperclips, etc.,*
- *vary the volume and pitch of your voice,*
- *be yourself (there is no need to act),*
- *be enthusiastic and smile.*

DON'T:
- *be tempted to race on; use pauses,*
- *speak to the blackboard, poster, etc. Look at the audience!*
- *read from your notes – speak naturally,*

Now that you have read this chapter try the student copymaster, Presentation checklist, on page 193.

Role play and drama

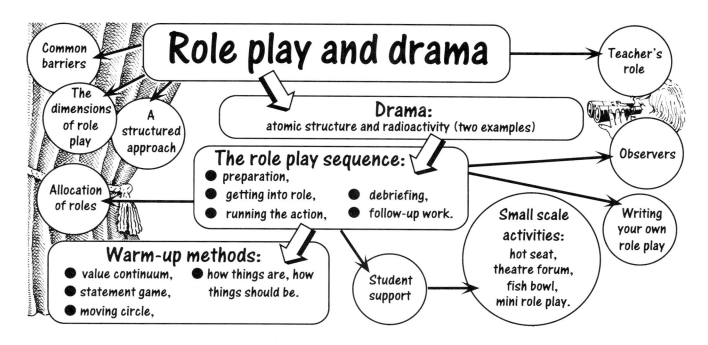

Role play and drama

Common barriers

The dimensions of role play

A structured approach

Allocation of roles

Teacher's role

Drama:
atomic structure and radioactivity (two examples)

The role play sequence:
● preparation,
● getting into role,
● running the action,
● debriefing,
● follow-up work.

Observers

Writing your own role play

Warm-up methods:
● value continuum,
● statement game,
● moving circle,
● how things are, how things should be.

Student support

Small scale activities:
hot seat,
theatre forum,
fish bowl,
mini role play.

Introduction

Why use role play and drama?

Role play and drama allow students to explore scientific facts and issues in a more motivating and realistic fashion. The gap between the classroom and everyday life is narrowed and the science becomes more meaningful. Students must use scientific data, knowledge and concepts to support arguments. In addition to this, communication and cooperative skills are developed.

Some of the benefits of using role play are displayed on the pinboard:

Benefits of role play:

- *explores view points,*
- *can help change attitudes,*
- *highly appropriate for dealing with controversial issues (see chapter 15, Introducing controversial issues),*
- *behaviour of student role is studied and not the actual student,*
- *students learn to control feelings and emotions,*
- *gives practice at various forms of behaviour and in various situations,*
- *learning is both very active and interactive,*

- *rapid feedback from both teacher and student,*
- *promotes group learning and cooperation,*
- *assimilates regular work but adds more interest,*
- *relates to real issues,*
- *highly motivating,*
- *encourages other activities, e.g. group discussion, reading, writing, project or extra-curricular work,*
- *helps focus on problems and their solutions.*

Role play covers three main areas:

- practices skills and techniques,
- explores understanding of scientific knowledge,
- explores views, feelings and attitudes.

It is possible to plan and organise role plays so that they cover all three categories. The combination of these is what makes role play such a powerful learning strategy.

ACTIVITY 7.1
Brainstorm a list of ingredients you feel a role play should have. Ask a colleague to do the same, and compare notes.

What is role play?

Role play varies considerably but most contain the same basic ingredients. By dissecting role plays into these ingredients it is easier to assess which elements make a worthwhile role play and how to solve problems that arise.

Role play ingredients

Place
Where is it happening?

People
Who is involved?

Time
When is it happening?
For how long?

Issue
What are they trying to understand?

Relationship
What is the relationship between people?

Common barriers to role play

Detailed information for overcoming the problems of using role play is given in later sections but some immediate responses to predominant worries are given in this section.

Students often don't have enough information

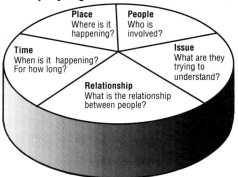

One of you will be a nuclear scientist, the other an x-ray crystallographer and then I want you to argue about the structure of DNA...

58

Reason for not using	Response
'Too time-consuming'	Use short role plays; use longer ones sparingly.
'Where's the science? I cannot justify the time needed'	Make science content and concepts important part of role play preparation.
'It is too frivolous – not serious science'	Ensure there is positive feedback and follow-up activity.
'Students are often embarrassed, or inhibited'	Allocate major roles and sub-roles carefully.
'They won't know enough – the role play will dry up'	Train students to make lists and agendas appropriate to their role.
'Things will get out of control – I cannot hand over class management to students'	Train, brief and trust students to follow rules. Develop your own management/facilitator role.
'My science lab is not suited to role play'	Plan furniture layout carefully, or find alternative venue.

ACTIVITY 7.2
Discuss with colleagues the teachers' function before, during and after a role play. Compare your findings to those we have given.

The teacher's role

The teacher has many, varied duties during a role play exercise.

These include:
- deciding what needs to be achieved. For example:
  - to heighten awareness of an issue,
  - to develop skills such as communication,
  - to promote tolerance of different view points,
  - to examine topic comprehension,
  - a mixture of these things,
- deciding what you want to focus on.

Having made these decisions you can then:
- provide a stimulus,
- provide background information,
- ensure adequate time for preparation, briefing and debriefing,
- control the timing of the role play,
- adjudicate,
- be enthusiastic, possibly getting involved with a minor role yourself,
- trouble-shoot – be aware of possible problems.

Using the strategy

The dimensions of role play

As with any new teaching or learning strategy the secret of a successful introduction to role play is to start on a small scale. Make initial role plays of short duration. Larger scale role plays can be attempted as circumstance and confidence dictate. It is important to remember that planning and preparation are vital, especially for the moment when students 'get-into-role'. Science teachers are used to detailed planning, i.e.

practical lessons, and role plays should be viewed in the same light.

There are a number of points worth considering before attempting a role play. These may be listed under three separate dimensions for convenience: the role player, the situation (or context) and the type of learning to take place.

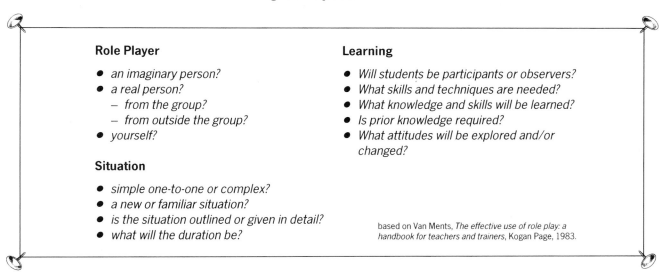

Role Player

- *an imaginary person?*
- *a real person?*
  - *from the group?*
  - *from outside the group?*
- *yourself?*

Situation

- *simple one-to-one or complex?*
- *a new or familiar situation?*
- *is the situation outlined or given in detail?*
- *what will the duration be?*

Learning

- *Will students be participants or observers?*
- *What skills and techniques are needed?*
- *What knowledge and skills will be learned?*
- *Is prior knowledge required?*
- *What attitudes will be explored and/or changed?*

based on Van Ments, *The effective use of role play: a handbook for teachers and trainers*, Kogan Page, 1983.

A structured approach to role play

The development of role play expertise can be looked at as a series of steps. This progression is outlined in the figure here:

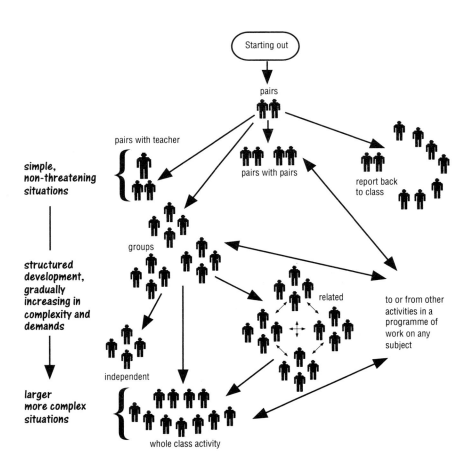

This does not mean that simple, short duration role plays involving two students are not useful, but, that such role plays are vital in preparation for more complex scenarios. The level of background knowledge and the degree of briefing rises with the complexity of the role play.

The role play sequence

Any successful role play follows the sequence in the flow diagram:

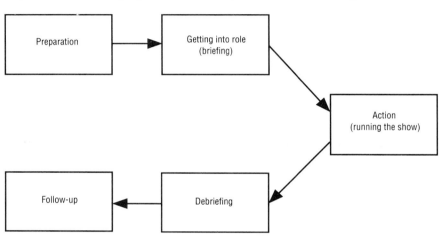

Preparation

Teacher's notes

- Consider the role play objectives.
- Decide on the type of role play.
- Provide opportunities for short, stance-taking exercises.
- Consider what stimulus you will use, e.g. video, audio tape, magazine, newspaper, quote, letter, case study, questionnaire, script from play.
- Decide whether you need a short, warm-up activity.
- Identify and clarify the issues involved; raise awareness and consider different perspectives.

- Supply students with necessary knowledge and understanding – try using small group discussion or active reading and writing for this.
- Use warm-up activities to establish views and knowledge, e.g. Value continuum, or Statements game (see pages 63–4).
- Introduce the role play gradually, perhaps using questions such as 'Can you give me an example of ...?', or 'What would the person do or say?'
- Allocate roles.

Getting into role (briefing)

Teacher's notes

- Get students to write or rewrite their role briefs.
- If role cards/briefs are given out students build up a better role picture if they:
  (a) underline views held by the character,
  (b) rewrite brief in the first person, e.g. 'I am . . .', 'I think . . .',
  (c) devise questions on the back of the role card to help develop the character,
  (d) 'work-up' characters in pairs
  — each person interviews the other, e.g. as a reporter interviewing an expert,
  — a list is made of how characters might feel or react in the situation
  Strategies such as Hot seat or Theatre forum (see page 65) can be used to practise roles.

- Involve all the students, albeit as reporters, observers, secretaries, recorders, union members, chemists, etc.
- If 5 or 6 roles are being used, form role groups to discuss each case, e.g. chemists, local residents, etc. (Resume mixed groups for the action stage.)
- Allow adequate time.

Running the action

Teacher's notes

- Students should be fully briefed and conversant with the situation, content, basic beliefs, feelings and attitudes to be enacted.
- Continuity is ensured only if there is thorough advance preparation. Students need to be fully 'in-role'.
- Use a suitable room and surroundings.
- Create a sense of occasion, particularly if using a grande scenario, or public enquiry approach.

- Generate an atmosphere of reality – use props but keep them to a minimum, e.g. name tags, telephone, tables, posters.
- Initiate the action and step back.
- Leave responsibility with the students.
- If you need to step in again, try to do so in-role.

Debriefing (in role)

Debriefing should be done while the students are still in-role. This way only the character or role is under attack, and not the student.

Teacher's notes

- Debrief in small groups (pairs, fours) particularly when exploring personal feelings in anticipation of a whole group discussion.
- Summarise what has been learned from the role play as you go. Orchestrate the discussion rather than saying too much yourself.
- Establish the facts and any decisions which have been reached.

Follow-up work (out of role)

Once students have been debriefed, and are out of role, get answers to the following questions:

- what do students think happened?
- how do they feel about their role and other peoples' roles?
- what decisions were taken and what do they think about these?
- what do students think they were trying to achieve?
- had they changed their views?

Try to analyse the cause of behaviour patterns during the role play. This is usually teacher-led, e.g. why did things happen the way they did?

Follow-up work might include discussion or activities on the following:

Follow-up work

- How role play findings can be related to real-life.
- How realistic the role play was.
- How the role play can help further study.
- What additional resources are needed for further study.
- What could be done? How does the role play fit in with current work?
- How useful it was in developing understanding of the issues and problems addressed.

Allocating roles

Roles can be assigned in a variety of ways, e.g.

- randomly
- the group decides,
- volunteers,
- key characters first,
- selection based on students suitability to purpose of role,
- students chosen according to their non-suitability to a role, particularly if it is advisable that they should experience a different viewpoint.

Roles may be rotated, once allocated, based on either new criteria or depending on how the activity progresses. Allocation of roles will also depend on whether there is a need for observer or assistant roles (pair work). Students working on a role in pairs can build confidence, help overcome shyness, and reduce the risk of 'drying up'.

Warm up methods

Value continuum

This is a useful technique to establish points of view on a particular issue or statement, such as 'you need alcohol to enjoy a social occasion'. One corner of the room is set aside for people of one extreme viewpoint and the opposite corner is designated for those people having the opposing viewpoint. Students are invited to place themselves along an imaginary scale between the two corners according to their opinion.

Variations:

- Students choose where they would **like** to be and not where they actually are.
- Each student explains why they have chosen a particular viewpoint.
- Split continuum in two and set up a discussion – one half tries to persuade the other to move across.

The value continuum method can also be used for sorting students into discussion groups, or to allocate roles.

The Statements Game

This is another useful technique for establishing points of view. Make short written statements on pieces of card on an issue of your choice. Number the statements and hand them around. Ask students to write against each statement, either **agree**, **not sure**, or **disagree**. The teacher can collect the cards and collate the views. The class can then discuss opinions on each statement, which although open to everyone, can still remain anonymous.

Variations:

- Students write statements themselves and arrange them in a long line. Students then sort these into groups representing different degrees of opinion (use a secret ballot if necessary).
- Obtain a range of statements from newspapers and magazines, or use famous quotes.

Moving circle

This method provides excellent practice at stance-taking and appreciating other peoples' viewpoints. Either as a class or in groups of around ten people, seat students facing one another in two circles – the inner circle facing out, and the outer circle facing in. Now give background information on the issue to be discussed. Students in the inner circle (A) must argue their case with their opposite partner in outer circle (B). After 2 minutes stop the discussion and ask the B's to move one place right and continue arguing their case with their new partner. After a further 2 minutes stop again and ask the B's to move once more to the right. This time, however, both A's and B's must reverse their stances and argue for another 2 minutes! This pattern (where stances are reversed every two rotations) should continue as long as the discussion necessitates it.

How things are, and how things should be

This is a useful activity for generating discussion in anticipation of a role play. Students draw two large overlapping circles on a piece of paper. An issue is chosen, and in one circle features of this issue in 'the world as I would like it to be' are described. In the other circle features of the issue in 'the world as it is' is described.

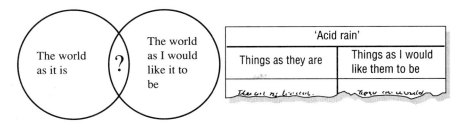

Alternatively, students can complete a table similar to the one shown. The activity can be done individually or in small groups, but either way it soon leads to discussion activity.

Student support in role play

There are many techniques for offering support to students before and during a role play exercise.

Role rotation
This gives more students a chance to experience key roles. It can be used to remove weak performers from role without loss of face.

Role reversal
Allows students to appreciate issues from another person's viewpoint. (Useful for controversial issues.)

Supporters
These are helpful if a role player dries up. Each player discusses their role with a group of students who can offer support later if it is needed.

Consultant group
The home or base support group (see chapter 3, page 28–9) acts as a team of consultants to advise a player on how to proceed. This can be very useful in the briefing stage, or for weaker performers.

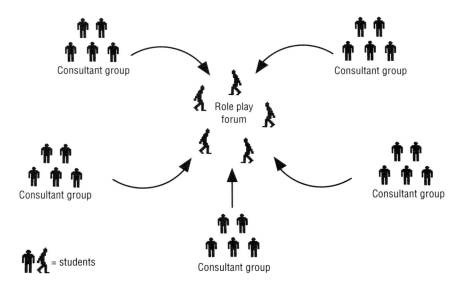

Small scale activities
Hot seat

This method is used either for role preparation or during the role play itself. Working in small groups of three to six people, volunteers take turns to position themselves in the hot seat and face questions on their role from other group members.

Theatre forum

This is also used for role preparation and during role play action. Two opposing players are selected from either a large group or two small groups and are asked to sit in a forum. The players argue their role stances. The remaining members sit in a circle around the players, and offer support if a player dries up. The players can exchange stances.

c

The fishbowl

This is an extended version of the hot seat. Two to four role players form a panel and are questioned by a small audience. This method can develop mini-conflicts and may require some teacher management to maintain its pace. Role players need to change places reasonably swiftly. It can also be used as a forum for the role play.

Mini-role play

This is essentially an ordinary discussion group except that three to five students discuss an issue in-role. It is most effectively run if groups are supplied with role cards. Students can write extended descriptions of 'themselves', 'their opinions' and 'attitudes' in preparation to the mini-role play.

Students work best with close friends on a topic which is very familiar to them. Ideally the issue should be put as a question and have a simple solution for reporting back, e.g. a poster or flow chart (OHP transparencies are also popular).

> *ACTIVITY 7.4*
> *Consider possible topics for the fishbowl and mini-role play methods.*

Writing your own role play

There are two important rules to bear in mind:

● Think small; think simple; think short.
● Keep your eyes and ears open for ideas, issues, and stimuli suitable for role play.

The role play copymaster Kinetic Theatre, on page 199 imitates the behaviour of particles.

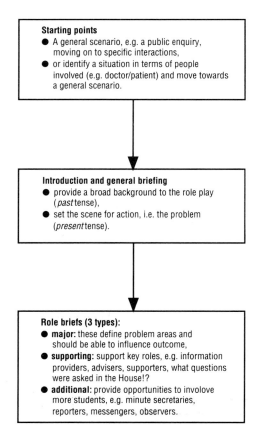

Starting points
● A general scenario, e.g. a public enquiry, moving on to specific interactions,
● or identify a situation in terms of people involved (e.g. doctor/patient) and move towards a general scenario.

Introduction and general briefing
● provide a broad background to the role play (*past* tense),
● set the scene for action, i.e. the problem (*present* tense).

Role briefs (3 types):
● **major:** these define problem areas and should be able to influence outcome,
● **supporting:** support key roles, e.g. information providers, advisers, supporters, what questions were asked in the House!?
● **additional:** provide opportunities to involove more students, e.g. minute secretaries, reporters, messengers, observers.

Writing the roles

In order to write roles, the advice of Van Ments (1983), summarised here, is very useful. Each role a student needs to act out, will essentially consist of a variety of features and courses of action characterised by the role itself. These are identified in the pinboard. General guidelines for teachers who have to produce role models are given in the clipboard.

Key features

- *knowledge and skills,*
- *motivation and beliefs,*
- *constraints and pressures,*
- *power and authority.*

Intended actions

- *who should characters meet?*
- *under what circumstances?*
- *to do what? for how long?*
- *what decisions must characters make?*

Writing a role

- Tell players their goals: what they are going to do, where, with whom, and for how long.
- Use sensible names.
- Use fictitious people and places, rather than actual, to avoid imitation.
- Write role briefs in the second person to internalise attitudes, e.g. 'you have'.
- Avoid describing emotions, e.g. 'you are very angry'.
- Keep role briefs short.
- Provide adequate time for role-familiarisation.

The whole class role play

- Arrange all furniture in a suitable fashion and settle role players into position.
- Set the scene, and remind students of the issue, their roles and their objectives.
- Set the level of formality. (A more formal atmosphere helps students to absorb and maintain roles.)
- Describe the rules of the role play.
- Announce the programme of events and consider providing an agenda.
- Formally announce 'the role play now begins'.
- Step back and allow the role play to flow.
- Interfere only if rules are broken. If interruption is necessary try to do so in-role.
- If the role play is not working, try to swop roles around.
- At the end of the role play, make sure thorough debriefing and follow-up exercises are completed.

Observers

Observers can offer support, encouragement and advice to students involved in role play. As an audience, observers create a more realistic atmosphere during enquiry or debate-type role plays. Observers can also evaluate or make records of role play action. This can be done **formally**, using a checklist or grid, or **informally**, perhaps as verbal feedback from an audience after a discussion or debate. An observers' checklist can be drawn up by the teacher, the role players, the observer, or by a combination of these.

An example of a checklist and grid are shown here. Both forms are invaluable for giving feedback to students and reviewing current learning. Information gathered can be invaluable to assessment.

Observers' checklist

Who spoke the most/least?

When did people interrupt before others had finished?

What questions/arguments were never answered?

How did the general atmosphere change during the session?

What other solutions were overlooked?

Did speakers maintain eye contact?

Did you feel each person was listening?

Were people encouraged to air their views?

How much manipulation was going on?

Did joking help or hinder the communication?

What signs of frustration, boredom, enthusiasm, etc. did you see?

Which members had high influence and which low?

Who kept the discussion on the rails? How?

Which actions helped the **task** (the problem being worked on) and which helped the **process** (the way it was being tackled)?

How were silences interpreted?

Who talks/doesn't talk to whom?

How were decisions made?

Did the group structure their use of time?

Were any issues side-stepped?

Observers' checking grid

Roles / Behavioural categories	Role A	Role B	Role C	Role D
Category 1	//	///	HHT	//
Category 2	HHT HHT ///	////	//	///
Category 3	//	HHT	///	HHT HHT
Category 4	///	HHT //		///
Category 5	//	///	////	//
Category 6	HHT	//	HHT	//

Source: Van Ments (1983)

Drama

The assumption that English and drama departments have sole ownership of drama activities should be questioned. Drama activities should be regarded as real opportunities to develop skills and knowledge in science situations. Keeping English and drama staff informed of your desire to develop drama techniques, and asking advice, can pay rich dividends. The following examples of drama activities linked to science have been provided by The Kinetic Theatre Company.

The two basic dramatic styles for teaching science actively are:

- simple role-play exercises in pairs or small groups,
- improvisation.

Atomic structure – an example of improvisation

The nature of the background research work for a study on the structure of the atom, will obviously depend on the age and ability of students. The method, however, is as follows:

- Supply a selection of badges in three colours for students to wear (say red, green and blue).
- Arrange students in groups and call these 'families'. Make certain there are an equal number of reds and greens in each group.
- Allow groups time to establish family relationships in ways of their own choosing (e.g. greens might be grandmother, blues mother, and reds sons or daughters).

- Gradually introduce stipulations such as:
  – greens and blues are lazy and won't move from their seats (perhaps they have overeaten and feel too heavy),
  – reds have argued and will not go near each other.
- Try to encourage students to establish their own reasons why these stipulations have been imposed. Allow time for further improvised dialogue.
- Add a further restriction: reds must find some reason for wanting or needing the greens, **but** the greens won't let the reds anywhere near them.

By this time the characters (students) should have developed firm relationships and organised themselves into the atomic pattern shown here:

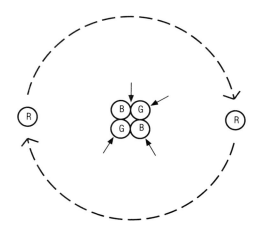

Key
R = red
B = blue
G = green

The exercise can take on many additional developments depending on what the teacher is hoping to illustrate, e.g. a red is kidnapped from one family by another (ionisation), or two groups share a red each to establish a bond between the families (covalent bonding).

Indeed, this is one of the beauties of improvisation technique, coupled with the fact that student enjoyment makes the scientific content so much more memorable. Last, don't forget debriefing and/or follow-up work.

Radioactivity – an example of a drama project

Dramatisation techniques involving scientific principles can be extended to include:

- small-scale play writing (by small groups for classes),
- larger-scale writing and production (e.g. by classes for performance at year-group assemblies),
- full-scale writing and presentation (for school performances).

Liaison between science and drama specialists at school will be a great help to all those concerned. The motivation instilled in students when making a larger production can be extremely beneficial to their study of science. The cross-curricular nature of these productions means that students with special talents, not necessarily related to science, can bring them to bear in scientific work.

The following activity, on radioactivity, is specifically intended for older, secondary school students. However, a wider range can study the results.

Imagine that students are given the assignment of providing an educational cabaret on the theme of radioactivity. The cabaret will cover both the historical development of radioactivity, and the nature of radioactivity itself. Research will obviously need to be done, and particular areas of research can be assigned to specific groups; for example:

Group	Area of research
1	The findings of Mme Curie
2	The work of Rutherford
3	The nature of alpha, beta and gamma radiation
4	Uses of radioactivity
5	The dangers of radiation

Once students have completed their background research, they can formulate ideas for a 10–15 minute cabaret sketch to illustrate their findings. Groups might come up with the following productions:

Groups	Possible cabaret production
1	A song and dance routine set in which Mme Curie is trying to persuade her husband that her findings are revolutionary.
2	A human 'ventriloquist-doll' of Geiger, sitting on Marsden's knee, relating the experiment details of how Rutherford identified the existence of alpha particles.
3	Alpha, beta and gamma particles applying for a job, with each particle promoting their own CV.
4	A hypochondriac insisting to their doctor that they need radiotherapy for some minor ailment.
5	An alien from outer-space has radioactive feet. Disguised as a human, at a dinner party, the alien's feet begin to smell!

The wide variety of possible ideas for a collection of amusing, yet informative, science-based sketches is endless. When the sketches have been finished, and satisfy the information born out of the earlier research, students can be allocated to the following groups, for the actual cabaret:

- performers,
- extras,
- costume designers,
- prop producers,
- lighting engineers,
- sound engineers.

Careful consideration needs to be given to the format of the cabaret evening, and a narrator may well be required (the science teacher?) to interline each sketch with additional information and to put the humour into serious context. Rehearsal time, performance dates and publicity will all need to be arranged, but what a difference a school production based on a scientific theme will make to *Oliver!*

Despite the extremely motivating and enjoyable nature of large-scale performances, the scale of involvement in science lessons will often be kept to small-scale play writing. At this level simple play-readings and script-writing can serve to motivate and inform individuals or small groups of students. Students can be given incomplete scripts and asked to fill in the missing words.

Theatre-in-education companies

Teachers wishing to extend the drama work within their science lessons can invite a drama group, such as The Kinetic Theatre Company, to give one of their interactive performances. These are extremely effective and great fun. Often material is specially written to cover science themes and issues which appear in the National Curriculum or GCSE syllabuses.

8

Information technology

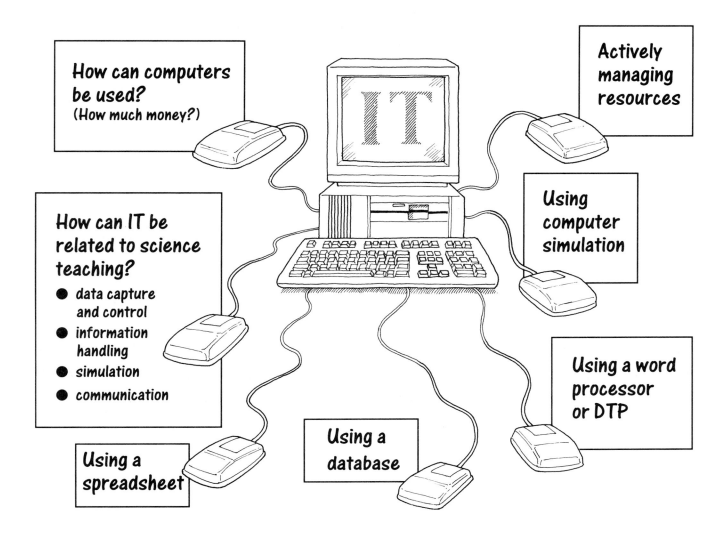

Introduction

Why use information technology

Information technology (IT) can be used to enhance and extend science learning. IT should encourage meaningful learning in science, based on active practical investigations done by the students, and emphasise the process rather than the specific content and knowledge acquired. Information technology should be seen as a tool to compliment and expand on existing learning activities, as opposed to designing course materials to fit the technology. IT may of course lead to new strategies and practices in the classroom.

Information technology skills are needed in light of the requirements set out in the National Curriculum for science. Computers, especially word processors, will also increase access to the curriculum for students with special educational needs. Concept Keyboards™ are particularly useful here.

How can computers be used?

Computers are ideal for monitoring experiments and handling large amounts of information. This enables students to concentrate on exploring science rather than tediously noting down repetitive sets of results or calculations. Computers offer more exciting ways of representing and displaying information and allow students to develop communication and presentation skills. They encourage group work and collaborative thinking, and put students in decision making situations otherwise impossible in the classroom. Computers also provide a way of extending science work into other curricular areas and beyond. The world is an open door, accessible through information technology.

Benefits of IT:

- Students can access and output information from a computer at different times during the lesson, e.g. with a database.
- Students can input information on to the computer at different times, e.g. using a spreadsheet, or word processing.
- A group of students can use the computer for a classroom investigation.

What do I need?

ACTIVITY 8.1
Find out what computing resources are available at your school in addition to any you have seen in the science department.

All the activities suggested in this chapter can be done on one computer system (e.g. a BBC micro, colour monitor, disc drive and printer), using relevant software and a kit of sensors with interface (more details later). A sophisticated network of sixteen computers and the luxurious surroundings of a computer room are **not** required. The computer should be with the action.

What will it cost?

Starting from scratch, the necessary equipment can be set up for around £1000. However, you might be able to use existing school equipment and your LEA computer centre can often help out with licensing of software or bulk purchases. Assuming you already have a computer system, software and monitoring equipment can be bought for about £100. The software adapts to many areas of the science curriculum, and you will not necessarily require specific software for each lesson. Concept Keyboards™, costing around £100, are excellent for special needs children.

How do I start?

Try to concentrate on one type of application and use it well, rather than attempting to do everything at once. Remember that you are using the computer to do a real job, not as part of a computer awareness programme.

Using the strategy

The key areas to be considered are:

- data capture and control,
- information handling,
- simulation,
- communication.

How can IT be related to science teaching?

Data capture and control

The use of sensing and monitoring instruments enables students to expand their observations and the potential of their investigations. Direct representation and data access give an immediate and striking feel to an experiment. This may lead to further ideas being tested. The technology allows a student to focus on what is actually happening rather than simply capturing results. Remote measurements on varying degrees of time scale can be made. These are particularly useful in environmental experiments. The real time representation of data also encourages active collaboration between students working in groups.

> **ACTIVITY 8.2**
> *Find out what sensors and software are available for data capture. Try some out if possible.*

In addition to collecting data the computer can be used to give instruction to devices being used in an experiment. A particular parameter or set of parameters can be controlled in this way, e.g. long term experiments in the fields of biology and biotechnology. Alternatively, this application can form an activity in its own right, perhaps with a design solution.

IT has many cross-curricular links with design and CDT departments. IT capability is AT5 of the National Curriculum for technology.

Information handling

Raw data from experiments does not readily display any useful information. Data has to be processed before it becomes meaningful. Many students experience difficulty with this aspect of learning. Allowing a computer to process results enables students to complete their investigations. The following packages are useful for this purpose:

- database,
- spreadsheet,
- graphing facility.

Each package can be used in different ways to support practical activities and investigation work. Spreadsheets, for example, can be of particular value to students interpreting data. The spreadsheet can be set up to manipulate experimental data into a form which is meaningful to students. The use of spreadsheets allows investigative work to be done on data collected. 'What if we change . . .?'-type questions can be asked and the results quickly displayed.

> **ACTIVITY 8.3**
> *Find out what information handling packages are available to use with your computer. Try some out if possible.*

Students are often asked to research new information in GCSE science courses. This can cause problems for some students and may lead to blind-copying from books. Databases which hold resource information and can be consulted are useful for this purpose. Indeed, a series of datafiles might well be constructed to serve this purpose. Students can develop their own datafiles to classify and organise information, possibly using results of practical investigation work. Group files can be compiled on individual research findings. This application of both database and spreadsheet is a useful method of collating class sets of results for further analysis. All of the packages described have the ability to produce graphs, which can be used to interpret results.

Simulation

There are occasions where the use of a computer simulation allows students to experience a situation they would otherwise not have been able to. By artificially changing factors they can observe the effects of, for example, pollution on an ecosystem or the output from a power generator when the pressure or temperature of the steam is altered. The activities should not replace standard classroom practice but can be used imaginatively to extend learning experiences. Look at the example on pages 79–80.

Look at the example on pages 79–80.

ACTIVITY 8.4
What computer assisted learning (CAL) packages suitable for simulation work do you have access to? Are they used? How can you find out how useful they are? Is there a catalogue with users' comments?

Communication

The display of student work is an important but often unemphasised part of science teaching. It is an area which can disenchant certain groups of students, leaving them with an overall impression of failure, even though they might have carried out a science investigation successfully. Graphics, word processing and desk top publishing (DTP) packages can all be used by students to reinforce communication skills. It is also worth considering other forms of electronic communication to display findings and precipitate interaction between students, e.g. viewdata, teletext. Communication skills are particularly relevant to students working in groups, especially where discussion is involved. The technology can be used to produce collaborative pieces of work, perhaps in the form of newspaper articles or leaflets. This type of work will reflect the cooperation and decision making skills involved in the task.

More and more schools are utilising systems such as Campus 2000, which allow them to communicate with other schools and organisations. Experimental data can be shared between schools and organisations across the country, and even abroad. The range of data is extended, which is particularly useful in environmental experiments. Just imagine, the whole world can be brought into the classroom!

Using a spreadsheet

A spreadsheet contains rows and columns of boxes (or cells) into which numbers, words, formulae, etc. can be placed. It is a flexible tool, which can do calculations on numerical data entered. Spreadsheets can be used:

- to help students draw graphs,
- to introduce the computer as a learning tool,
- to extend investigations.

Take, for example, an experiment to measure the individual reaction speeds of a class. The reaction time is measured by recording the distance a ruler falls between the students' fingers before it is caught (repeated three times). A spreadsheet can be used to process the abundance of results, thereby incorporating information technology into an otherwise standard practical activity. The flow diagram illustrates how the experiment can be orchestrated by the teacher.

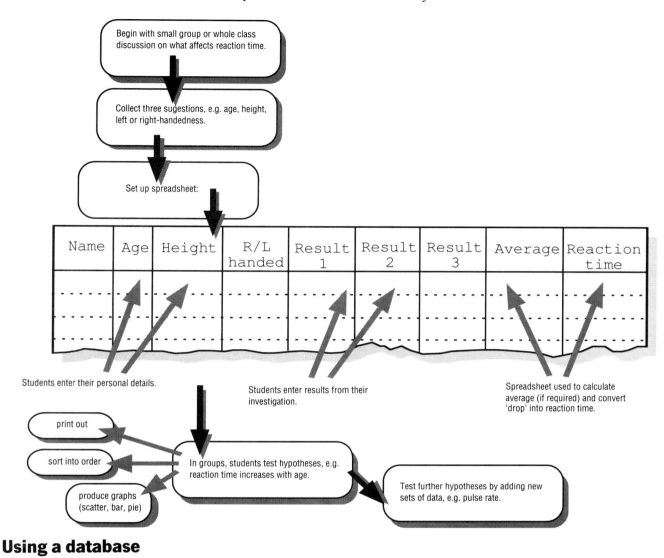

Begin with small group or whole class discussion on what affects reaction time.

Collect three sugestions, e.g. age, height, left or right-handedness.

Set up spreadsheet:

Name	Age	Height	R/L handed	Result 1	Result 2	Result 3	Average	Reaction time

Students enter their personal details.

Students enter results from their investigation.

Spreadsheet used to calculate average (if required) and convert 'drop' into reaction time.

print out

sort into order

produce graphs (scatter, bar, pie)

In groups, students test hypotheses, e.g. reaction time increases with age.

Test further hypotheses by adding new sets of data, e.g. pulse rate.

Using a database

What is a database?
A database is a series of electronic cards stored on a computer. They list information under headings, similar to a card index in a library.

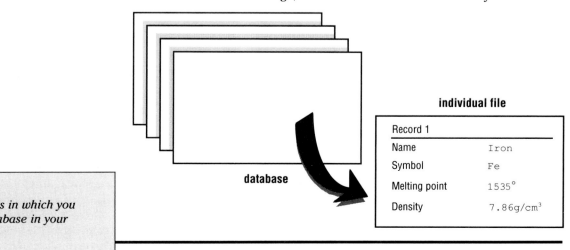

individual file

Record 1	
Name	Iron
Symbol	Fe
Melting point	1535°
Density	7.86g/cm³

database

ACTIVITY 8.5
Brainstorm ways in which you could use a database in your science classes.

76

Why use one?

Databases:
- allow students access to prepared files of information on a range of topics,
- can be used to collect information from student investigations,
- allow searching, sorting and graphing to be done quickly,
- allow students to test hypotheses using their data.

When can one be used?

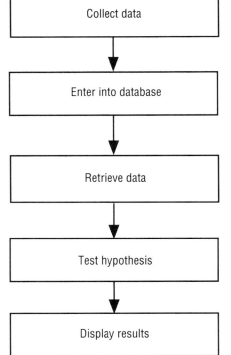

- Collect data
- Enter into database
- Retrieve data
- Test hypothesis
- Display results

Databases are useful:

- *to collate material during class investigations,*
- *to research topics,*
- *to test hypotheses at the end of an experiment.*

A typical lower school science activity for measuring body dimensions and looking variation in these can be supported, and enhanced, using a database. Students collect data as normal, but enter it on to a database. Either in groups or individually, students can use the database to investigate relationships between quantities and test hypotheses. Questions such as 'Are tall people heavy?', 'Does leg length affect stride length?', and 'Do blue-eyed people have blond hair?' can be tested. Display features (graphs etc.) of the database can be used to communicate findings. A computer's ability to store data allows class, year group and even school files to be created. This is particularly relevant to recording progression through the age range.

A branching database

An example of using the computer to support a fairly standard science activity is described here. The example uses a branching database.

A lower secondary school science class are looking at ways of classifying things. The teacher has exhibited a collection of objects, intended to form the basis for a study on biological classification and keys. The objects are all plants and animals (in various preserved forms!). The exhibition stimulates discussion at the beginning of the lesson – students are naturally inquisitive. The discussion should be brief, concentrating on the differences and possible groupings of the exhibits. No definitive solutions are requested at this stage. The class is divided into groups of about four and each group is asked to choose a certain number of objects from the exhibition (say two per person). A group's first task is to carefully study their objects and write down a list of ten observations on each. The observations are crucial to identifying differences later in the process. Groups are told that they will have to make a display of their work later, which they will present to other groups.

The computer is introduced as a means of sorting the objects. A binary splitting program (in this case Branch) is used. The software is simple to use. Students must ask questions which divide the objects into two groups.

These questions must require only a yes or no answer, e.g. 'is it?', 'can it?', 'does it?', etc. The splitting process is repeated until all objects are unique.

The program only structures the process; the students supply all the information. A 'go to' key, which will contain a series of instructions to help classify objects, can be printed out at the end. Students are encouraged to try their keys out on other groups in the class. They generally need little encouragement!

Back in groups, away from the computer, the exhibition can be completed but with the objects now sorted and a key alongside. Students often convert the key into a 'tree' diagram with their questions and answers forming the branches of the tree.

Time on the computer can be shared and fitted in with the various stages of the activity. Most groups complete the sort in 15–20 minutes, but this will need monitoring. The choice of objects will depend on the topic being covered. The questioning sequence often leads to further investigations – perhaps testing a collection of materials to see if they float, or conduct electricity.

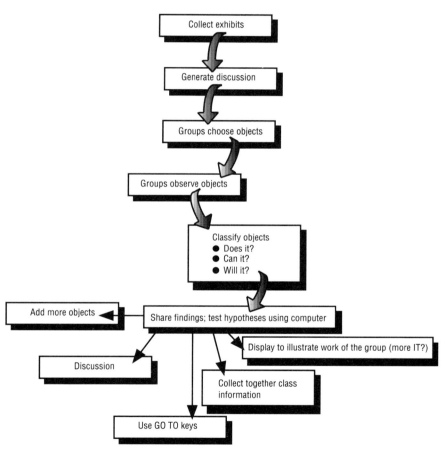

Using a word processor or desk top publishing system

ACTIVITY 8.6
Find out what word processing and desk top publishing packages are available to use with your computer. Try some out to see how user-friendly they are.

What are word processing and desk top publishing?

Word processing uses the computer as a typewriter but has many more features, e.g. changing text, saving text, layout, etc. Desk top publishing is more sophisticated. DTP packages combine word processing with the ability to add graphics and features such as different type faces.

Why use these?

Word processing and DTP:

- develop a variety of communication skills,
- consolidate learning,
- encourage collaborative work.

When can these be used?

Word processors and DTP systems are useful

- *for writing group reports on investigations,*
- *for active writing, e.g. newspaper articles, marketing reports, letters,*
- *to assist students with learning difficulties.*

How can these be introduced?

Introducing word processing and DTP

- Start with simple word processing activities, e.g. Folio, Prompt writer, Pendown.
- Use the standard system for the school so that students familiarise themselves with one system.
- Do not concern yourself with using all the features and facilities on the system.
- Do not teach the skill – use word processing and DTP as a means to an end.
- Let the skills develop as needs arise.

If students have difficulty typing in and spelling new scientific vocabulary use an overlay in conjunction with a Concept Keyboard™ for unfamiliar terms.

Using a computer simulation

An excellent example of a computer simulation is the Nuclear reactor simulation package produced by the UKAEA. Students are required to operate a simulated nuclear power generating plant. The program is interactive since the student is asked to make decisions based on numerical and graphical information. However, simply sitting one or two students in front of a computer screen is only a very passive use of this resource. It is better to enter into the spirit of the activity and plan a nuclear reactor session, possibly even a day if timetabling allows. A role play type activity can be developed in which students take on the following roles:

Group 1: the power station engineers

The engineers control the reactor. It is important for them to run through the program beforehand, to familiarise themselves with the effects of changing control rods, coolant speeds, etc.

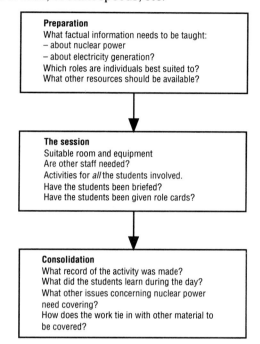

Preparation
What factual information needs to be taught:
– about nuclear power
– about electricity generation?
Which roles are individuals best suited to?
What other resources should be available?

The session
Suitable room and equipment
Are other staff needed?
Activities for *all* the students involved.
Have the students been briefed?
Have the students been given role cards?

Consolidation
What record of the activity was made?
What did the students learn during the day?
What other issues concerning nuclear power need covering?
How does the work tie in with other material to be covered?

Group 2: the electricity generating board

The briefing session for these will concentrate on estimating and predicting demand. Activities on planning and feeding information to the power station may be needed.

Group 3: the consumers

Consumers monitor their own needs and draw up a list of pros and cons concerning the use of nuclear power.

Group 4: the environmentalists

Environmentalists monitor the performance of groups 1 and 2 and draw up a list of the environmental pros and cons of using nuclear power.

This can be performed by twelve students, divided up into four groups of three. Students react to the information given by the simulation according to which role they assume.

The teacher can ask each group to produce a poster or OHP transparency summarising their performance during the simulation/role play. Students can give a short presentation to the rest of the class explaining their standpoint.

Computer monitoring and control

With the appropriate sensors, interfaces, and software a computer can be used as a monitoring or control device. Data-logging instruments are an excellent example of this. With the aid of a computer they can receive data directly from experiments and present it in an accessible form. A portable data logger, such as Sense and Control, which allows data capture to take place away from fixed power points, gives added freedom to lesson planning.

The ability to monitor situations over a long period of time and collect large amounts of data provides opportunities for work on differentiated tasks. The introduction of data-logging devices encourages the replacement of individual or class practical work by project work. Groups of students can each investigate a specific aspect of the work and pool their results later. Students are given the opportunity to work cooperatively, communicate more effectively, and solve problems in a real way.

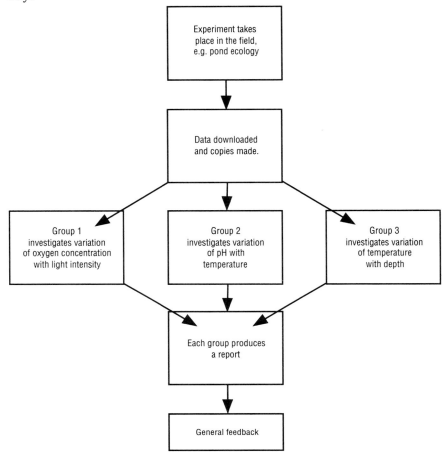

Actively managing resources

We have seen that there are a number of different ways of using the computer actively in the classroom. The actual management of hardware and software needs consideration. Many simulations allow students to save their work. It is important to make use of this facility. Timetable students so that they have time at the computer when it is needed but do not waste this time doing research elsewhere. Provide students with discs to save work on. The same applies to investigational activities using spread sheets or databases. Last, set up facilities for printing out information, results and graphs so that students can leave the computer terminal and investigate the science behind the work.

Information technology has many benefits in science learning, providing resources are used and managed in an imaginative and active way. It is hoped that students will achieve a greater understanding of both science and IT when using computers during lesson time.

Resources

The following resources are useful for activities suggested in this chapter.

Software	System or programme	Available from
Databases	DIY (BBC, Arc, Nimbus) Find (BBC, Nimbus)	RESOURCE Exeter Road, Doncaster, DN2 4PY Tel. 0302 340331
	Key (BBC) Key Plus (Arc)	ITV Schools 6 Paul Street, London, EC2A 4JH
	Branch (BBC)	NCET University of Warwick Science Park, Sir William Lyons Road, Coventry, CV4 7EZ Tel. 0203 416994
Spreadsheets	Grasshopper (BBC, Nimbus) Arc	Newman College Genners Lane, Bartley Green, Birmingham, B32 3NT Tel. 021 476 1181
Datalogging	Sense and Control (BBC, Arc, Nimbus)	Educational Electronics 28 Lake Street, Leighton Buzzard, Beds. LU7 8RX Tel. 0525 373666
	Measure-IT (BBC, Arc, Nimbus)	RESOURCE (see address above)
Simulations	Nuclear reactor	UKAEA Education Service PO Box 10, Wetherby, West Yorks. LS23 7EI

9

Visits, visitors and field trips

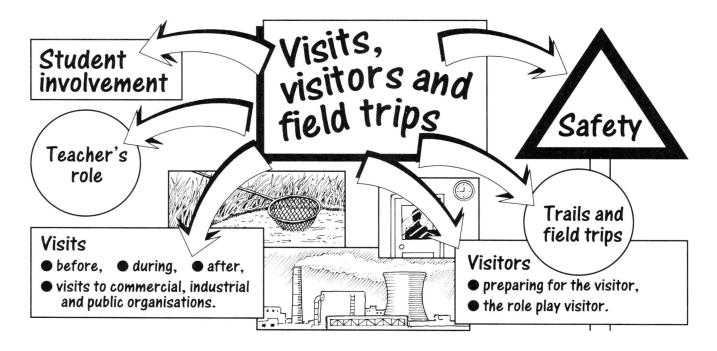

Student involvement

Teacher's role

Visits, visitors and field trips

Safety

Trails and field trips

Visits
- before,
- during,
- after,
- visits to commercial, industrial and public organisations.

Visitors
- preparing for the visitor,
- the role play visitor.

Introduction

Why arrange visits?

Scientific experiences should not be confined to the school laboratory. An increased awareness of the role of science in industry and society is beneficial to a student's education. Visits can provide this, and also are informative and motivating. The opportunity to take students to a local factory or exhibition to see science in action should not be missed.

What can visitors add to our science teaching?

A well-informed visitor, on a purposeful visit, gives students valuable first hand experience of the way science is used in industry, commerce or research. Economic awareness is also developed (see NCC circular 6). Meeting visitors allows students to practise social skills and raise career issues.

Are field trips worth the bother?

Field trips certainly require careful organisation, but the benefits to students are immense. Real life experiences have more impact, and many activities cannot be carried out in the laboratory, e.g. studying variations in local habitat.

Does the National Curriculum allow time for trips and fieldwork?

The National Curriculum documents clearly state that fieldwork should form an integral part of the science curriculum:
'Pupils should investigate by observation, experiment and fieldwork, the properties and formation of igneous, metamorphic and sedimentary rocks' (key stage 3, AT3).

'Pupils should study a variety of habitats at first hand' (key stage 3, AT2).

'They should have opportunities through fieldwork and other investigations, to consider current concerns about human activity' (key stage 4, AT2).

'Pupils should study, through laboratory and fieldwork, the evidence which reveals the mode of formation and later deformation of rocks' (key stage 4, AT3).

Do legal problems make trips impossible?

Recent publicity concerning student accidents cannot be ignored, and teachers who take students out of school bounds are responsible for their safety. However, with careful planning and sensible checking the safety risks during a visit can be minimised.

Student involvement in these activities

ACTIVITY 9.1
Brainstorm factors which lead to (a) a teacher-led visit, (b) a student-owned visit.

Having recognised the need for visits, visitors and fieldwork it is important to write them into the science curriculum. Identifying topics that would benefit from this approach is a relatively simple matter. Thorough planning and a sense of ownership by the student will give maximum value from the activity.

Now look at the ideas we have suggested in the table. (A similar sort of table can be drawn up for visitors, or field trips.)

Teacher-centred visit	Student-centred active visit
Teacher announces visit and its purpose.	Students brainstorm the purpose of the visit and its relevance to coursework.
Teacher plans visit and makes all arrangements. A worksheet is prepared.	Groups of students discuss and plan the stages of the visit. A series of activities is planned and information is sent for about the place to be visited.
Teacher and/or guide take students around the visit site as students fill in a worksheet.	Students are directed around during the visit, as they complete their worksheet, checklist, etc. A variety of activities and tasks are carried out.
Students hand in worksheets for the teacher to mark.	Students report back from the visit. Follow-up work in the form of experiments, displays and projects is encouraged.

The teacher's role

An active approach to visits and visitors casts the teacher into a different role. You are no longer the organiser of an event in which other people act as the audience. Your role is to prompt discussion and assist with planning and preparation. Students will develop a share in the activities, and a vested interest in their outcome. The experience and expertise of the teacher is still important, but allow students to do as much as they can. Whether this extends to students contacting visitors or destinations directly, or working through you as a liaison officer is a matter for your own judgment.

Making the transition

The move towards student ownership of visits and responsibility for visitors can be made step-by-step. Students can begin with the planning of a mock visit. The students need to be informed that a visit will not take place, but the planning skills are important to future visits. This way motivation is maximised. The advantages of prior knowledge, planning, and reporting back are all considered.

Once students are competent at playing an active role in visits it is important to give them the opportunity to practise this. Try starting with short visits to the local community (in small groups) before arranging visits to larger, commercial concerns.

Using the strategy

Visits

Before the visit

Try to identify the reason(s) for visiting a particular place, or organisation:

- to stimulate interest in a science topic?
- to acquire specialist information for a project or optional topic?
- to increase knowledge of equipment and techniques used in industry, and not available in school?
- to raise industrial awareness?
- to obtain careers information?

The teacher should try to involve students in the choice of visit, e.g. by writing letters, making phone calls, etc. Companies need to be primed about this as all too often, and understandably, they will not deal directly with students.

Students must then sort out which information needs to be gained from the visit. Questions can be rehearsed in small groups, perhaps with groups taking responsibility for a particular function of the company, e.g. background, finance, sales, research and development. Individual groups might be made responsible for finding specific information during the visit, so long as all groups get to see the exciting bits!

Planning should be in consultation with the appropriate representatives. Personal contact is important. Teachers will be more able to direct the planning of the visit if they have first-hand experience of the place to be visited. Consider a small pre-visit. It is also helpful if the representatives can visit the school beforehand to brief students, perhaps with brochures, slides, or photos of what is going to be seen. This gives time to digest information and breeds familiarity with the intended visit. Talks given on-site are often not effective by themselves, but in conjunction with a pre-visit briefing they provide useful revision. It also helps if students can recognise machines or operations without having to be told during the visit.

The scope of the visit should be limited. Too much information, particularly if it is of a technical nature, overwhelms the student and causes confusion. As a rough guide the time limit for one plant, one process should be around 1–2 hours.

Allow sufficient time for a visit!

Last, inform governors and parents of visits as early as possible and keep them informed. The governing body will need to give consent. If payment is required, check with the school policy on this. If a visit is to be privately funded devise a system of collecting money, giving receipts and banking monies promptly. Be careful not to let too much money accumulate at school. Many LEAs (and schools) have strict regulations controlling this. Prepare a balance sheet.

During the visit

Visits must be active experiences rather than 'look and listen' sessions.

Will the visit be stimulating?

During a visit:

- Hand out worksheets and questionnaires.
- Set tasks on site, e.g. data gathering, finding information to solve real problems (those facing the company, observation tests, etc.)
- Provide a flow sheet for processes so that students can follow real-life stages.
- Allow opportunities for informal discussion with operators and other staff.
- Make sure guides face the students and are audible.

- Ask students to report back on specific tasks.
- Constant checking, and regular headcounts, are wise precautions. If groups are allowed to move freely it is only sensible to have reporting back times.
- Display posters which may assist understanding at relevant locations on the tour, e.g. detailing an industrial process (especially if it is noisy!)

After the visit

Once the visit is over, arrange time for debriefing and follow-up work. It is important to make sure this is done. It is very helpful at this stage if a rep visit the class again for a summing-up session and question forum. If this is not possible, the teacher must do this. Students do not find it easy to formulate questions during the visit and may need time to reflect on the knowledge they have gained. Posting questions to the visit location after the visit can be very productive. The questions should accompany a thank you letter, which should be sent anyway.

Visits to commercial, industrial and public organisations

There is a growing acceptance in science education that young people should be aware of the role played by industry and science in society. A very effective way of heightening this awareness is to develop partnerships between schools and industry which at some point involve students themselves liaising with company representatives, e.g. arranging a visit as an integral component of the science curriculum.

The National Curriculum requirement for students to have an understanding of the nature of science and to appreciate the historical development of scientific ideas can be met, in part, by museum visits. The rich variety of resources can be used actively to explore how evolving theories have changed peoples' scientific ideas, moving away from more traditional history. As with all visits the key to success is careful planning and maximum student involvement.

Pre-planning is vital!

But it says only one bus here.

A programmed or structured visit differs from the traditional factory or museum tour in that:

- the teacher (with pupil involvement) plans the visit, and familiarises his- or herself with the place to be visited,
- students have an itinerary and programme of work,
- it involves lesson-work prior to the visit. This may involve students helping to plan and organise the visit,
- follow-up work, based on information obtained during the visit, is encouraged. Industrialists or museum staff can be included in this.

Visitors

ACTIVITY 9.2
List the visitors you think can contribute to your science lessons.

Although this technique has been used extensively as a social technique in schools, it is also an invaluable learning tool for science programmes. Whatever the reason is for inviting a visitor to school, students gain far more from the session if they are actively involved in conducting it.

The range of possible visitors is almost endless: other members of staff, students with interesting hobbies, parents, medical personnel, public figures, police, trade union representatives, university and polytechnic staff, industrialists, etc. However, not all visitor sessions are successful. This is usually due to lack of preparation on behalf of the group or visitor. A visitor to a class must be sensitive to their particular difficulties and help overcome them.

Initially, the prospect of a visitor is suggested by the teacher: 'Shall we have a visitor to the group?' As the teaching programme progresses, ways in which visitors can be usefully employed often arise naturally from the work. Stimulus for such work can be found in the student copymaster, Local noise problems – arranging a visitor (page 207).

Preparing for a visitor

- *Who do we invite and for what purpose?*
- *Who will make the invitation? In writing or in person?*
- *What do we talk about?*
- *How can we make sure everyone says something?*
- *How do we prevent individuals dominating the visit?*
- *Can we ask personal questions?*
- *Where is the best place to meet?*
- *Do we provide refreshments? Who looks after these?*
- *How do we greet the visitor?*
- *Where will the visitor sit? Where will the class sit?*
- *How do we bring the session to a close?*
- *Who will thank the visitor?*
- *Who will escort the visitor back to reception?*
- *How do we review the visit?*

There is usually a natural progression towards a series of questions that need answering, when preparing for a visitor. The lively discussion and small scale role plays that grow from this work ensure that everyone is clear about what will happen and what is to be said. Students will also feel more confident. Since it is unlikely that groups will consider all the relevant questions, especially if they are inexperienced, prompt questions should be prepared.

Preparing for the visitor

The visitor may be just as nervous as the students...

Preparation in anticipation of a visitor attending the school is vital. The whole process must be reviewed with the students. The group may wish to discuss the scientific questions to be asked and organise who should put them to the visitor. Understanding the objectives of the visit, and the visitor's background, will enable students to achieve maximum value from their questions. Basic issues can be covered before the visitor arrives to allow more time to discuss specialised points. Since it is unlikely that groups will consider all the relevant questions, especially if inexperienced, prompt questions should be prepared to stimulate discussion.

Preparation on the visitor's behalf is just as important. The visitor needs to know a little about the nature of the group and the work they are doing. Brief the visitor on the type of questions they can expect to meet. Preliminary questions may be a little stilted and visitors should be requested not to talk at length or fill in for small silences which crop up. This will also avoid by-passing some of the questions students have so carefully prepared.

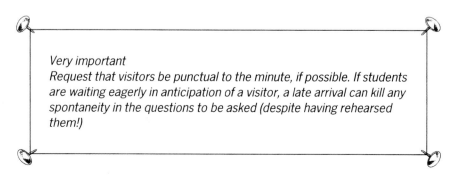

Very important
Request that visitors be punctual to the minute, if possible. If students are waiting eagerly in anticipation of a visitor, a late arrival can kill any spontaneity in the questions to be asked (despite having rehearsed them!)

Teachers sometimes put-off their first visitor session, saying 'My group isn't ready yet.' Avoid doing this – don't delay! Experience has shown this to be a most unifying exercise, often the point at which groups 'take off'. The teacher's hardest job when a visitor arrives, is to sit back and leave it all to the students. One of the most rewarding moments comes when students gather around afterwards, bursting to talk about their experience, and share a corporate sense of 'didn't we do well'. Last, don't forget the debriefing – it is essential to review the science learning that has resulted from the visit.

The role play visitor

Role play visitors are a viable alternative to actual visitors. However, the task of preparing a visitor of this nature can be quite taxing for students. Time needs to be given to role research and preparation of the 'visitor'. The teacher can help this preparation by designing visitor role play cards which outline personal details and brief life history, etc. The research process can be done by individuals or in groups.

Once the role is researched the next step is to decide whether the class are told who the visitor is, or whether they have to identify the visitor by questioning. This technique is especially useful for studying the lives and work of deceased scientists. Indeed, it forms the basis for a fascinating look at their ideas. The method has been used very successfully to introduce advisers, advisory teachers and student teachers to groups they encounter in their profession. Naturally, practice at this method will be required.

Students are pleasantly surprised at the results they acheive from talking to visitors. Students mature in their own eyes through the willingness of a visitor to speak freely with them, and are often eager for another visit to take place. The visitor contribution to learning is considerable. Students also realise that visitors can be nervous too!

Trails and field trips

Educational trails and fieldwork necessitate the teacher taking groups of students out of school grounds, sometimes for extended periods of time. In this respect they resemble visits. The guidelines stated in the visits section concerning consultation with governing bodies, informing parents and banking money apply equally here.

Trails

For the purpose of this chapter trails are defined as any drive or walk along a predetermined path to examine areas of interest that are clearly marked *in situ* or on a map or plan. There are two types of trail that can be used in an active learning sense:

- commercially produced trails,
- teacher and/or student produced trails.

Commercial trails

Commercial trails are mapped out by a wide variety of organisations such as library services, local societies, National Parks, the Forestry Commission and publishers. Points to consider when choosing one of these are as follows:

- Does the trail cover the area of science you wish to study?
- Is the trail in an accessible geographical area?
- Is support material accessible to all students? Will it need modifying for readability?

- Is the trail active enough? Many trails involve active walking, but little active science.
- Is the trail within the physical capabilities of **all** students?
- What preparation is needed? Will students need to absorb a lot of information prior to the trail? Do students have the necessary skills?

Are the students physically capable of completing the trip?

Come on Y9, just 7 kilometres to go!

The two main problems with commercially produced trails are that they can never be tailor-made to a particular school, and the students have no ownership. However, the trails are generally well presented and remove a lot of the preparation work from the teacher.

Making commercial trails active

- Guides to commercial trails can be modified by students before they embark on the trail, e.g. sections of trail can be rewritten as questions designed by the students.
- Information can be omitted from trails, so that students have to complete missing details during the visit (or produce their own alternative trail).

- Student-owned activities can be written into the trail, e.g. testing rock types, measuring flow rates of streams.
- Follow-up work needs doing and could include:
  - extending information given in trail leaflets,
  - written reports on the trail,
  - designing new trails,
  - modifying trails for sight-impaired people.

Designing trails

Teacher and/or student produced trails are more difficult and time consuming to prepare, but they are potentially more rewarding. The advantages of 'home-made' trails are that they directly reflect lesson work, can be organised near to the school and give students a sense of increased motivation through ownership.

The designing of a trail can involve as much, if not more, learning than actually following it.

Designing trails

- Allow students to identify trail objectives.
- Make sure students understand why a trail is being prepared, the science content, and the processes involved.
- Give trails added purpose and status by getting groups to follow trails designed by their colleagues.
- Share work out using the jigsaw method – see chapter 3, Group discussion (talking and listening). Groups can take responsibility for particular geographical or scientific areas.
- Tailor teacher input according to level of experience, e.g. supply trail plan but ask students to design activities.
- Ask students to compile list of necessary accessories, e.g. clipboards, stop-watches, thermometers.

Examples of trails in the school locale

Material trails
Many building materials, shop fronts, etc. can be seen close to schools, or even within school grounds. A trail of these can link the properties of the materials to their use.

Energy trails
Examples of fuels and energy changes around us are extremely common, e.g. petrol and diesel powered vehicles, traffic lights, shop window displays. A trail within school is also possible on this subject – radiators, lights, cookers, scientific apparatus, etc.

Ecology trails
From lichen to flower displays, parks to parking areas, there is a huge pool of information that can be drawn upon to study how plants and animals behave, their habitats and human influence on them.

Speed and friction
Road safety, vehicle speeds, vehicle design, road surfaces, tyres, car safety columns, motorcycle helmets – all these and many others are just outside the school gates. Many of these can be linked directly to problem-solving activities within the laboratory, e.g. testing materials, designing safety helmets.

There are vast numbers of other topics that form a sound basis for a trail, including simple machines, bridges, noise levels, insulation and playgrounds. Useful ideas for this can be found in the article S. Foster, *Streetwise Physics*, (SSR, 1989), Vol. 71, No. 254, p. 15–22.

ACTIVITY 9.3
List some field trips you could organise for work you are doing this term.

Field Trips

Field trips vary enormously in duration, from an afternoon visit to the school playing field to a couple of weeks studying the geology of an unfamiliar region. The scope of a field trip will depend on the teacher, but the points on the following page are relevant to any type of field work.

Field trips

- Students must know the objectives of the field trip and should get involved in the planning stage.
- Focus on a few specific areas of study.
- Keep walking to a minimum and activities to a maximum!
- Produce support materials, e.g. maps, or labels and text for posters.
- Consider splitting up students into expert teams to study specific areas (see pages 29–30).
- Encourage students to photograph things.

- Evaluate field work by asking students what they gained from the work, how much they enjoyed it, and how their contribution added to the success of the visit.
- Follow-up work should be done as soon as possible. However, restrict evening work on residential visits. Students get very tired doing the actual field work.
- Give follow-up work high status. Problem-solving, data searches, report writing and display work can all be pursued back at school.

ACTIVITY 9.4
Jot down a list of possible types of field work in your local environment.

Examples of field work

- Soil studies and rock identification can usually be carried out within or near to school grounds. Many buildings, e.g. banks, contain various types of rock in their decorative exteriors.
- Building sites and excavation works provide excellent opportunities to study soil layers and underlying rocks. Coastal outcrops and quarries are also extremely useful places to view rock layers. Examples of erosion on bedding, jointing and folding can usually be seen. Samples may occasionally be removed without damaging the site.
- Weathering and erosion may be studied locally. Buildings, gravestones, and walls are all affected by acid rain, weathering and erosion. Footpath erosion may be just outside the staff room window!

- Any stream or river can be used to study water purity, pH, flow rate and fauna and flora. A stream can be adopted as a study area and cleaned as part of an environmental project. Traffic surveys can be used to raise awareness of airborne pollutants in the environment.
- Weather and pollution monitoring can be set up either at or near to school.
- Local farms are excellent places to study modern farming practices and their effect on the environment.

There are many other examples of how field work can enrich the education of students. Two student copymasters for you to try are Out on the trail, on page 205 and Noise patrol, on page 206.

Safety

Recently, there has been a great deal of publicity concerning school visits that have ended in tragedy. A lot of criticism has been levelled at the staff involved. Taking students out of the school environment, even for short periods of time, places increased responsibility on staff and this should not be ignored. The following guidelines are useful:

- Obtain written permission from governors and all parents.
- Inform parents of the following: dates, duration, purpose, destination, method of travel, cost, insurance, equipment required, staff accompanying trip, plus the name and home phone number of a staff contact **not** going on the visit.
- Obtain details of special medical requirements for any students. (Consent is needed to give treatment.)
- Check all students are insured for personal injury and offer personal property insurance as an option.
- Confirm with governors that the chosen insurance is adequate, especially if an LEA scheme is not being used. Request written confirmation to this end.

- Obtain written confirmation that the visit is being organised and undertaken 'on behalf of the employer' and that governors agree it is of educational benefit.
- Check guidelines on educational visits and journeys issued by the LEA and DFE (available in all schools) and conform to these.
- Consider taking out personal liability cover yourself.
- If applicable, ensure that staff are qualified to take students to the chosen destination, e.g. mountain leader certificate if visiting hilly or mountainous areas.
- Ensure that both female and male staff are present on mixed gender visits.
- One member of staff should have a first aid certificate.
- Advise on sensible clothing. Check that any specialist clothing used actually fits the students.

The following additional points should be noted for visits to areas that could be described as hazardous:

- Check weather forecasts.
- Beware of mist and sudden weather changes on high land. Carry a map and compass – **know** how to use them.
- Winter is an especially dangerous time for walking in upland areas. Icy slopes and avalanches cause numerous accidents each year in Britain, even in the most innocuous looking regions. Winter walking is best left to the very experienced leaders.
- Water-proof and wind-proof clothing, as well as spare clothes should be carried by all members of the party if they are going to be walking long distances in sparse terrain.
- Correct footwear is essential. Vibram type walking books are ideal; wellington boots and training shoes are potentially dangerous. Get advice.
- Extra food and drink should be carried on long walks.

- **Always** leave word of where you are going, the number in the party, and when you expect to return.
- On coastal walks beware of tidal changes and warn students of the dangers of cliff-climbing.
- Ensure that **all** members of the party are capable of completing the walk or visit. This is essentially a case of planning for the **least** fit.
- Make sure all members of the party follow the Country Code.
- Take a first aid kit.

The guidelines may seem off-putting but they are only common sense. If followed correctly the organisers and participants will be well prepared to tackle both the expected and the unexpected. Remember that trips do not **have** to be in the wild and woolly mountains and shores of Britain. Consult the list of further reading at the back of this book, for more advice in these matters.

10
Data handling

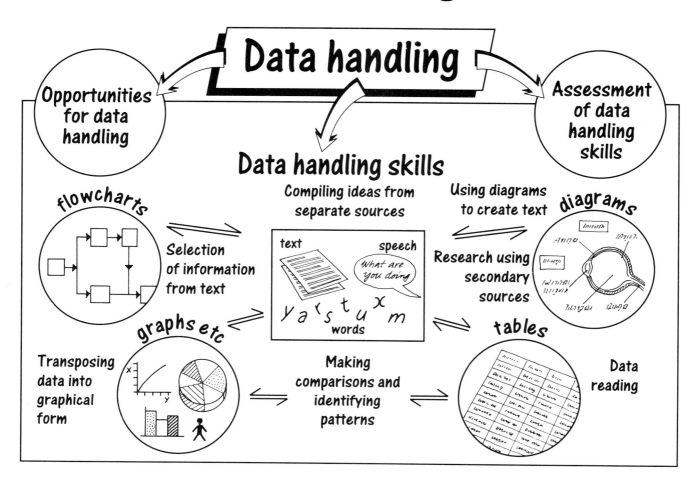

Introduction

Why use active data handling?

Scientific data and information can be presented in a variety of forms, and it is important, both in the study of science itself and in everyday life, to be able to interpret these. The skills and abilities involved relate to the assessment of students for the National Curriculum and GCSE.

How can the strategy be used effectively?

ACTIVITY 10.1
Brainstorm all the different activities in your science lessons which involve data handling. (The diagram on page 97 gives some ideas on this.)

The development of data handling skills does not require the introduction of additional content into science courses. Students encounter data and information virtually all of the time in science. Consequently there are many opportunities in existing courses to develop data handling skills.

To develop data handling skills, thought needs to be given as to **how** data and information are presented and to what students are expected to do with it. Students should do more than simply memorise information in the form it is presented. They need to select, transform and reorganise data in some way. This more active approach will not only develop data handling skills but will also enhance the understanding and retention of scientific concepts and relationships.

How can data handling be assessed?

Conveniently, the activities which allow students to develop data handling skills are the very same activities which are the most appropriate for assessment.

What does data handling involve?

Data handling involves a variety of skills.

ACTIVITY 10.2
Before reading any further jot down what you think data handling involves. What skills are your students going to need if they are to handle data successfully?

Data handling:

- *increases familiarity with ways in which scientific data and information are presented;*
- *helps students to select the most appropriate form of presentation of information;*
- *enables students to convert data from one form to another;*
- *helps students to recognise patterns;*
- *encourages students to select and reorganise data and information for a particular purpose.*

Are data handling skills accessible to all students? Careful selection of data handling activities, and careful structuring will ensure positive and credit-worthy responses at all levels. Teachers can give progressively stronger clues to solutions until students are able to make final decisions themselves.

Using the Strategy

Opportunities for data handling

Students do not need to spend a lot of time practising data handling skills as a separate component of their science education. Students should be given frequent opportunity to deploy and develop these skills during the normal course of the work, when scientific data needs to be processed.

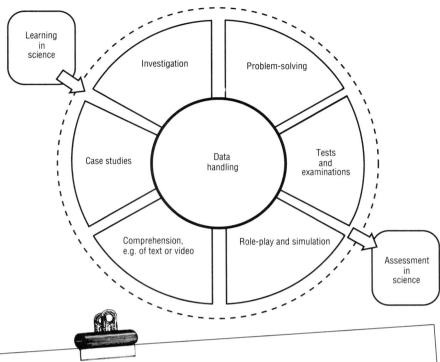

Many components of science education involve data handling

Data handling opportunities present themselves when:

- students are studying diagrams, flow charts, graphs, tables, etc.
- students are carrying out investigations; instructions to unfamiliar equipment or techniques need to be understood, and data must be presented in a suitable format.

- students are solving problems; information relevant to the problem-solving activity needs to be selected.
- students are doing case studies, role plays or simulations; familiarisation with background information is necessary, which often needs to be put in a form that has greater impact.

In all of the points listed, students are required to use data and information **actively** to develop a greater scientific understanding. A range of other scientific skills will also benefit from this approach. Data handling activities are likely to be far more motivating if done in the context of a relevant or worthwhile task, rather than as isolated, somewhat arbitrary exercises. Wherever possible students should reorganise and/or present information in a different form to ensure that it is fully understood.

ACTIVITY 10.3
Which specific activties in your current teaching schedule lend themselves to the development of data handling skills?

Try presenting students with information which is **not** in its most appropriate form and ask them to improve on it.

Discussion between students, and between teacher and student, is an effective way of developing data handling skills.

Data handling skills

Look at the first page of this chapter. You will see that data handling involves a number of different skills:

Data handling skills:

- *understanding that data and information can be presented in different forms, e.g. words, diagrams, flowcharts, tables, line graphs, pie charts, bar charts, histograms,*
- *converting data from one form to another,*

- *selecting appropriate software,*
- *interpolating, extrapolating and finding patterns in data,*
- *researching data for a particular purpose,*
- *presenting data in the most suitable form.*

ACTIVITY 10.4
Review the development of data handling activities at different levels. How can you make activties easier for students who have difficulty handling data? How can you make the activities more challenging?

All of these skills can be developed at a variety of levels. The remainder of the chapter looks at these, together with suggestions for contexts in which to develop them.

Transposing data into graphical form

The following modes of display are implied when we refer to graphical form: pie charts, bar charts, histograms, line graphs.

This skill can be deployed and developed:

- when presenting data obtained in first-hand investigations,
- when presenting information from a role-play brief as effectively as possible.

Some useful guidelines are as follows:

Transposition of data is made easier if:

- the graphical form is specified,
- axes and/or scales are supplied,
- some points/bars/sectors are already plotted,
- all points/bars/sectors fall on marked scales,
- any line graphs are straight and fit exactly,
- all the points are 'true',
- the line is an exact fit,
- appropriate ranges are provided for any histograms.

Transposition is more challenging if:

- the graphical form needs to be decided,
- axes and/or scales have to be constructed,
- no points/bars/sectors are plotted,
- points/bars/sectors fall between marked scales,
- the line is curved,
- a 'rogue' point needs to be ignored,
- the line is a 'best' fit,
- appropriate ranges have to be selected.

Try student copymasters Crops and climate (page 209 and Who's the fitter (page 210) on using data to plot graphs.

Reading data

Students need to read data from tables, pie charts, bar charts, histograms, line graphs, etc. Reading skills can be developed during problem-solving activities, case studies and role plays.

Data is read easily if:

- it falls neatly on to marked points on a scale,
- the data required from pie charts, bar charts, histograms, etc., requires no manipulation,
- the necessary data in line graphs and tables falls within the given ranges.

The reading of data is more challenging if:

- it falls between marked points on a scale,
- sets of data must be combined to produce the required data,
- extrapolation is needed from the supplied data.

Making comparisons and identifying patterns

These skills can be deployed and developed:

- when interpreting data generated in first-hand investigations,
- when interpreting established data (if first-hand invetigation is impracticable).

The tasks are made easier if:

- only a qualitative response is required,
- a relationship is linear,
- two variables are directly proportional,
- there is regular periodicity,
- for histograms, only the mode has to be identified.

Tasks are more challenging if:

- a quantitative response is required,
- a relationship is non-linear,
- two variables are inversely proportional,
- there is irregular periodicity
- distribution has to be described.

Try the student copymaster Can I stop in time (page 206).

Using diagrams to create text

These skills can be deployed and developed:

- when encountering new ideas in, for example, text books,
- when writing a commentary on a chart or diagram.

The tasks are easier if:

- diagrams are conceptually simple,
- only a few items need to be transferred,
- the number of items is known,
- support grids and/or tables are given.

Tasks are more challenging if:

- diagrams are conceptually complex,
- there are many items to transfer,
- the number of items is unknown,
- support is not given.

An example of this technique is the comparative study of a laboratory process with the corresponding industrial method; perhaps the extraction of salt. Students are asked to compile a flow chart of the industrial production of salt. Textbooks or videos can be studied for this purpose. Once this has been checked for accuracy, a labelled flow chart of the laboratory process is supplied. Students are then given the task of explaining the two in a written account, outlining any important differences between each process. By completing this exercise, students both compile a flow chart from printed text (or video) **and** write an account using diagrams.

Selection of information from text

Written work often needs to be analysed and then represented in one of the following forms:

- answers to questions (a 'comprehension'),
- diagrams, e.g. of structures or mechanisms,
- flow charts, e.g. of processes or procedures,
- tables.

These skills can be deployed and developed:

- when familiarising students with new information and ideas, e.g. using textbooks,
- when digesting information presented in a brief.

The process is simplified if:

- questions are phrased similar to how they are in the text,
- questions are in the same order as the text,
- the text is short and/or simple,
- a diagram, headed table or other response has to be completed.

The process is more challenging if:

- questions are phrased differently to the text,
- question order is different to text order,
- the text is long and/or complex,
- a table, diagram or response has to be constructed.

The material on DARTS in chapter 4, Active reading (see page 35) may also be helpful here.

Compiling ideas from separate sources

The important thing here is that students are presented with a mixture of items that need sorting into something more coherent. This is likely to be the case if students have to:

- describe a process or practical procedure,
- explain why something happens,
- explain how something works,
- argue a case.

The skills can be deployed and developed:

- in preparation for a practical investigation (the steps must be correctly sequenced first),
- when encountering new ideas from secondary sources. (Ideas can be deliberately dismantled for students to reconstruct.)

The task is easier if:

- there are just a few items or sources of information (say a maximum of four),
- all the information needed for a complete response is given,
- all the information provided is relevant,
- a particular point of view is to be argued (remember to stress other views in conclusions and follow-up work).

Tasks are more challenging if:

- there are a lot of items or sources of information,
- information needed for a complex response is omitted,
- irrelevant information is included,
- a balanced judgement is required.

Research using secondary sources

These skills can be deployed and developed:

- when preparing a case study,
- when researching a new or controversial aspect of science and technology.

The task is easier if:

- detailed references are provided,
- only a small set of reference resources are needed.

The task is more challenging if:

- specific references are not made,
- an extensive range of resources need consulting, e.g. a whole library.

Assessment of data handling skills

In the assessment of data handling skills, it is important to recognise that they are sometimes referred to under various headings. The National Curriculum for Science refers to systematic recording, interpretation and evaluation of collected data; using mathematical relationships; developing computer skills for collection, storage and analysis; and the handling of data from secondary sources.

Earlier we mentioned that the same activities can be used for the development *and* the assessment of data handling skills. However, there are some important differences to note. In an examination or test, we can only be sure that we are actually testing data handling skills and abilities if we use **unfamiliar** material. Otherwise, students simply recall memorised interpretations. Second, if students fail a question which requires **both** recall **and** interpretation of data, it may not be their ability to handle data which is deficient. To assess data handling skills 'recall-free' items are needed. (Often misleadingly referred to as 'content-free'.)

Of course, when students are studying a new area in science, the content is at that point unfamiliar to them. This situation is similar then to that used in assessment when recall-free items are used. Data handling in the learning situation, however, will usually be more or less incidental to some larger activity and can often presume knowledge of the work which has preceded it. For the reasons given above, this presumption will not normally be made in the assessment situation using recall-free items.

11

Problem-solving

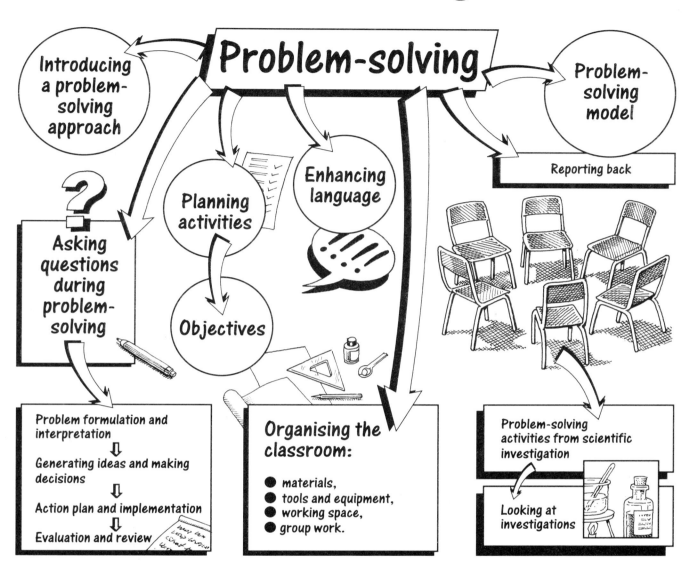

Problem-solving

- Introducing a problem-solving approach
- Problem-solving model
- Reporting back
- Planning activities
- Enhancing language
- Objectives
- Asking questions during problem-solving
  - Problem formulation and interpretation ⇩
  - Generating ideas and making decisions ⇩
  - Action plan and implementation ⇩
  - Evaluation and review
- Organising the classroom:
  - ● materials,
  - ● tools and equipment,
  - ● working space,
  - ● group work.
- Problem-solving activities from scientific investigation
- Looking at investigations

Introduction

What is problem-solving?

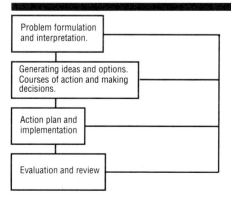

- Problem formulation and interpretation.
- Generating ideas and options. Courses of action and making decisions.
- Action plan and implementation
- Evaluation and review

Problem-solving is an investigative approach to learning. The technique does not form a separate subject within the curriculum, nor is it a strategy solely applicable to one or two areas. A problem-solving approach should be adopted as a continuous process, and as a basis for teaching and learning in all curriculum subjects.

Students are not immediately engaged in problem-solving simply by asking them to tackle an exciting task. Problem-solving requires students to use a variety of skills to acquire results. Students must also monitor this process continually in order that they may solve problems more effectively in the future. Students need to understand the problem-solving process. This may be represented in a four-stage model:

Why use problem-solving?

Knowledge has doubled in the last decade and will probably treble in the next. We are no longer in a position to teach content by merely providing facts. Children must be given the opportunity to develop a broad range of learning skills in order to equip themselves to meet the demands of the twenty-first century. The ability to recognise, analyse and solve problems is an increasingly important life skill.

What are the major benefits?

Problem-solving is possibly the most powerful of all active teaching and learning strategies at the teacher's disposal, yet it can also be the most problematical. Teachers who have used problem-solving successfully are enthusiastic advocates of the strategy.

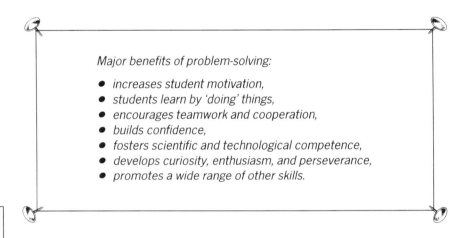

Major benefits of problem-solving:

- *increases student motivation,*
- *students learn by 'doing' things,*
- *encourages teamwork and cooperation,*
- *builds confidence,*
- *fosters scientific and technological competence,*
- *develops curiosity, enthusiasm, and perseverance,*
- *promotes a wide range of other skills.*

ACTIVITY 11.1
Before looking at the illustration, jot down what skills you think problem-solving requires, and reinforces.

There is little doubt that problem-solving both **requires**, and at the same time **reinforces**, a wide range of desirable skills.

All of these skills are put to use in problem-solving. Effective problem-solving, however, requires students to learn these skills. It is therefore sensible to give students opportunities to practise the skills by doing short, selected exercises.

Problem-solving is more than just working through an investigation or task. It can be used as an over-arching strategy to enable students to make a wide variety of things happen for themselves.

Decision making

Whole brain thinking:
- logical, analytical,
- creative, imaginative.

Selecting, handling and processing information

Predicting, reviewing, controlling, evaluating, explaining, drawing conclusions

Planning, negotiating, organising.

Setting and achieving objectives (making things happen)

Cooperative group work,
- team work,
- supporting one another:
- self-responsibility.

Communication:
- discussion,
- presentation,
- active reading/writing.

A fundamental aspect of this strategy is the continual monitoring, control and evaluation by students of their work. Students take on more responsibility for their learning which becomes more student-centred. A problem-solving approach enables the teacher to introduce a more flexible learning system into the classroom.

Do science teachers use problem-solving already?

For many years, science teaching has moved steadily towards a more investigative approach. It is less common to witness lengthy class demonstrations, or the monotonous completion of 'exercise 28' in the text book today; but how much work is of a genuinely investigative nature? How often is investigation so tightly constrained that it can lead to only one outcome? To what extent are these investigations little more than a disguised procedure? There should always be plenty of opportunity for independent thinking, original ideas, genuine investigation, exploration and discovery, within the bounds of problem-solving activities.

How can a problem-solving approach be sure to cover content?

ACTIVITY 11.2
Look at a National Curriculum topic you have taught recently and consider possible ways in which a problem solving approach might be helpful.

The National Curriculum clearly states the need to learn scientific concepts and knowledge. Some teachers are apprehensive about an open-ended, broad-based approach to learning because they are worried that scientific information will not be conveyed. A combination of careful monitoring and control, will see that the teacher ensures coverage of scientific content, whilst allowing children to learn for themselves.

How does a teacher's role change?

In a problem-solving situation the teacher dictates knowledge far less, and allows students to find information out for themselves. The teacher assumes a facilitator role, and gives guidance to students only when necessary.

Teachers can set a wide variety of practical tasks, ranging from a step-by-step recipe of instructions to a completely open-ended problem, perhaps identified by the students themselves. The figure below explores the relationship between the type of task and the subsequent teacher involvement.

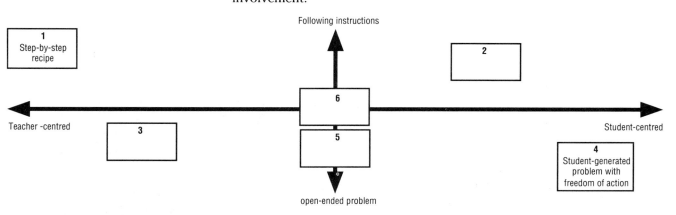

Adapted from: R. Lock, *School Science Review*, Vol. 71, No.256 (SSR, 1990)

ACTIVITY 11.3
With a small group of colleagues try to describe the type of practical task categorised by boxes two to six in the diagram.

The type of practical work which the teacher provides will depend largely on the purpose the students are to pursue. The extent of its open-ended or problem-solving nature will depend on the level of teacher direction or control. R. Lock, *School Science Review*, Vol. 71, No. 256 (SSR, 1990) identified five key questions relating to the planning of practical work:

- Who defines the area of interest?
- Who states the problem?
- Who does the planning?
- Who decides on the strategy to use?
- Who interprets the results?

The more the above questions are answered with 'the students' the more **open-ended** and **student-centred** the problem-solving will be. Lock suggests that with a lot of courses now striking a balance between process and content, there is a strong case for a wide variety of teacher/student control in practical work patterns. Equal priority should be given to providing practical work in which the answers to only one or two of the questions is 'students', and work where the answer to all the questions is 'students'. As students develop problem-solving skills and gain confidence the teacher's role will move from orchestrator to facilitator. You may also find it helpful to consider the range of possible roles a teacher can assume if the problem-solving activities suggested in the National Curriculum for Science (examples) are carried out.

Using the strategy

Introducing a problem-solving approach

To introduce a practical problem-solving approach, it is necessary to take account of the students' previous experiences, and their preconceptions of what is expected of them in science lessons. A little time is needed for students to come to terms with this new learning style. The context of activities needs to be carefully selected so that it forms a natural and integral part of the current programme of work. Isolated 'great-egg-race' challenges on Friday afternoon are not synonymous with an on-going problem-solving approach. The following outlines how this can be done:

1 Provide regular opportunities for students to engage in a variety of problem-solving tasks.

2 Try to instil in students:

- **confidence** – remind them they are already experienced problem solvers and have been solving problems all their life!
- **enthusiasm** – problem-solving is fun,and challenging.
- **cooperation** – working in a team, sharing ideas, and talking problems through, leads to more satisfactory results.
- **responsibility** – each person must take responsibility for their contribution to the team effort. This will increase the commitment to and desire for success.
- **a 'whole-brain' approach** – students must be logical, analytical, but use creative, imaginative and intuitive skills as well!

3 Try to dispel:

- the fear of making mistakes,
- the 'one-right-answer' syndrome,
- the desire to rush headlong into problems without stopping to think or plan.

4 Make sure that tasks are approached in a systematic manner. Break the problem down into a series of ordered and essential steps:

- Clearly identify the problem, what is to be achieved and the criteria for judging success.
- Plan a range of ideas and designs, and carefully select the most promising.
- Draw up a detailed plan of action and implement it.
- Review and evaluate. Try again if necessary.

5 Once a more systematic approach has been 'internalised' through practice, training and reinforcement, students are more likely to apply it to scientific problems, and problems in everyday life.

Good Problem Solver

- *Thinks first!*
- *Clearly identifies the problem and decides what needs to be achieved.*
- *Discusses a range of ideas and designs. Selects the most promising.*
- *Listens to other points of view.*
- *Plans a course of action and carries it out.*
- *Has method or purposeful approach.*
- *Asks 'can it be done better?'*

Poor Problem Solver

- *Rushes headlong into action without identifying the problem.*
- *Does not plan in detail.*
- *Makes repeated false starts.*
- *Does not listen to views of others.*
- *Accepts inadequate results or solutions.*
- *Has no method or purposeful approach.*

Poor problem solver...

Good problem solver

106

6 Planning process sheets (PPSs) can be very helpful during problem-solving invetigations. They serve to remind students of the essential steps that lead to effective problem-solving, while assisting students with their investigations. Four sheets should be adequate, covering the four main stages in the problem-solving process. PPSs also provide a means of monitoring and assessing the students' progress.

Planning process sheet 1: the problem

- *What is the problem; what needs to be achieved?*
- *Why is there a need to solve the problem?*

- *What things does the problem depend on? What do I need to find out about these?*
- *What information and materials are available to solve the problem?*

Planning process sheet 2: planning ideas

- *What ideas and designs do I have for solving the problem?*
- *What are all the things that can be changed or tested?*
- *What will happen if I follow each idea or design?*
- *Which course of action seems most promising? How do I decide this?*

Planning process sheet 3: planning the investigation

- *What is the chosen plan?*
- *What equipment or information is needed? What is available?*
- *What is my checklist or schedule for carrying out the plan? How will I control the investigation?*
- *What will I record and how?*

Planning process sheet 4: checking results and methods

- *What do the results tell me?*
- *Does the solution solve what I set out to do? Can it be improved? How?*
- *Do I need to try another idea or design?*
- *Did I follow the plan and did the group work well together?*

Detailed planning is time-consuming but as students become well versed at it, the process takes less time, runs smoother, and is inherent in the students' thinking. Eventually, students will be capable of developing their own PPSs, or even solve problems without them.

7 Problem-solving can be very structured to begin with, but as students become confident at it, attempt more holistic, open-ended problems.

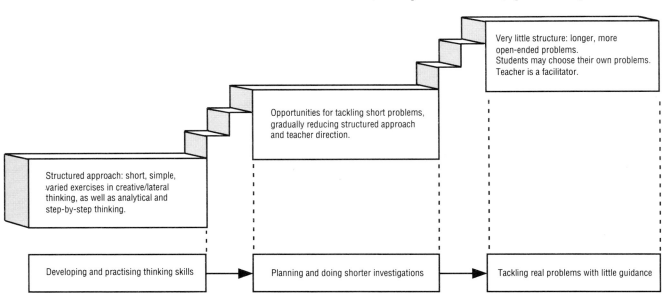

Structured approach: short, simple, varied exercises in creative/lateral thinking, as well as analytical and step-by-step thinking.

Opportunities for tackling short problems, gradually reducing structured approach and teacher direction.

Very little structure: longer, more open-ended problems.
Students may choose their own problems.
Teacher is a facilitator.

Developing and practising thinking skills → Planning and doing shorter investigations → Tackling real problems with little guidance

8 Wherever possible, try to set problems in the broader context of everyday life. This makes problem-solving exercises more relevant to the student, and ultimately more purposeful.

It is not our intention to suggest that teachers prescribe each stage in a problem-solving exercise so that students follow a chosen path to a particular solution. However, a system for tackling problems needs to be developed which concentrates students' thinking and planning, whilst harnessing creativity, inspiration, resourcefulness, and intuition.

Asking questions during problem-solving

Most questions asked by teachers are of a closed nature, usually to ascertain routine information or to test recollection of facts. Few questions are sufficiently open to challenge the student. The cornerstone to problem-solving is a well-chosen question. Why? what if? and how? are powerful tools in developing an enquiring and investigative mind. Teachers much ask **themselves** questions, as well as the students. Ask yourself:

- What are the objectives?
- What are the most appropriate methods of achieving the objectives?
- How may they be presented to students?
- How should the class be organised?
- What resources are necessary?

Before introducing an activity, ask students:

- What their experience or understanding of a topic is.
- How they can find out more.
- Can they do anything to help?

Encourage students to question their own group's activities. For example:

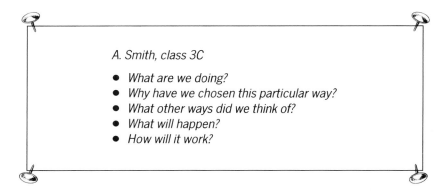

A. Smith, class 3C

- *What are we doing?*
- *Why have we chosen this particular way?*
- *What other ways did we think of?*
- *What will happen?*
- *How will it work?*

Ask open questions as much as possible. Open questions:

- demand that the teacher adopts a position alongside the student, not knowing but wishing to find out,
- do not elicit a specific response, but broaden the scope for alternatives, and lead students to consider different possibilities,
- offer opportunities to think about an issue rather than leap at answers,
- help to dispel the 'one-right-answer' syndrome.

ACTIVITY 11.4
Think about a topic you have recently taught. Jot down the questions you asked your students. How many of these were open questions and how many closed?

Some helpful questions for each problem-solving stage

Problem formulation and interpretation

For the teacher:

- What is the problem?
- Why is there a problem?
- What needs to be achieved?
- Why does a problem need solving?
- What difficulties present themselves?
- What factors does the problem depend upon?
- What needs to be found out about each of these? Where can you look?
- What information and materials are available to solve the problem?
- What else may still need to be found out?
- How will you know when the problem is solved?
- Does cost and/or time matter?

To the student:

- State the problem in your own words.
- Describe it to someone else.
- Draw or picture it.
- Think what you are going to do.
- Picture the obstacles and then the result or solution you need.
- List all the parts to the problem, or circle the words 'the problem' on paper and draw in all the parts around it.
- Brainstorm things that may be useful to find out about each part.
- Write down what you know about these and what needs to be found out.
- Make a list of resources available to you.
- Discuss the problem – share it!

Generating ideas and making decisions

For the teacher:

- What ideas or designs do you have for solving the problem?
- What factors can be changed or tested?
- What will happen if you follow a particular idea or course of action?
- Which course of action seems most promising? How will you decide this?
- Does it 'feel' right?

To the student:

- Keep an ideas diary.
- Brainstorm ideas – be logical, analytical, creative, and imaginative.
- Look for connections between different parts of the problem.
- Use a topic-web or mind-map to show relationships.
- Narrow your options to a shortlist.
- Decide which options meet essential and which meet desirable criteria.
- Of the options remaining, list advantages and disadvantages, and subsequently give each option a score from one to ten points. Use these to help you reach a decision.

Action plan and implementation

For the teacher:

- What is the chosen plan?
- What needs to be varied and what needs to be kept constant in the investigation?
- What information or materials are needed?
- What needs to be recorded and how?
- Who will do what?
- How long will the work take?
- How will you keep a check on investigations?

To the student:

- Allow sufficient time to draw up an action plan, including safety precautions.
- A topic-web is useful for drawing up a plan of the individual activities or investigations.

Evaluation and review

For the teacher:

- What do the results tell you?
- Does the solution match what was expected?
- How do you know this?
- Could this be improved? How?

To the student:

Evaluation/review checklist (score from 0–10)
- How do you rate your group's result?
- How well do other groups rate it?
- How far did you follow your plan?

- Did you follow the plan?
- Did your group work well together? Did everyone contribute?
- Does another design need to be tested?

- How well did you work as a group?
- Could your result have been better?
- Would you do it differently again?
- Did you enjoy the experience?

Planning activities

The following points outline the nature of the activities which may be used in problem-solving.

Activities for problem-solving:

- Match activities to your objectives. They may be designed to introduce, develop or apply a particular concept in a new or familiar situation.
- Make activities relevant to the programme of study; re-examine, restructure, or represent existing practical work.
- Activities should be challenging, not necessarily challenges.
- Ensure that all necessary resources are available to tackle an activity.

Objectives

A teacher needs to be clear about the objectives of a problem-solving exercise when choosing an activity.

For example, is the activity for:

- introducing a topic?
- introducing a new concept?
- developing a concept?
- applying a familiar concept in a new situation?
- developing particular skills, e.g. researching or hypothesising?
- using 'fair-testing?'

Some activities are more suited to introducing concepts. An example of this is the 'fast-thinker' problem, for which a problem must be solved within a given time limit. Other more long-term activities are suited to the development of a concept.

Take, for example, the subject of road safety. The teacher can use a 'fast-thinker' problem to introduce the relationship between speed, distance, and time. Students are asked to let a marble roll from the top-left-hand corner of a sloping board to the bottom-right-hand corner in a specified time. There is a range of possible solutions to this problem, many of which control the descent and fine-tuning the speed and the distance the marble has to travel. As a follow-up to this, students are asked to construct a vehicle which can be loaded with different masses. Students then measure the speed, total distance travelled and force required to bring the vehicle to rest, if it has been released from the top of a slope. The relationship between the sets of data collected and the implications for road safety can be considered.

Role play can be used to bring another dimension to this activity. Students could be:

- research engineers for an HGV manufacturer,
- a local council requested by residents to consider introducing vehicle weight restrictions through a village centre,
- a group of MPs considering a Bill to increase the maximum loading weights for HGVs,
- road safety officers working to create a demonstration for a mobile school exhibition.

Consult chapter 7, Role play and drama for advice on running role plays.

Enhancing language

The problem-solving approach, particularly when applied to practical situations, enhances language, confidence and understanding:

- questioning encourages students to explain, listen and respond,
- co-operative activity involves higher levels of disussion, debate and expression of ideas,
- reporting back develops confidence and presentation skills,
- development of technical vocabulary forms a basis for understanding concepts and principles in science.

Organising the classroom

> **ACTIVITY 11.5**
> *Storage of miscellaneous materials can be a problem. How can a wide variety of oddments be stored at your school? Discuss with colleagues (or students) which system will give greatest accessibility.*

Materials

Practical problem-solving activities demand greater material resources than a simple collection of glassware, chemicals and weights. Investigative learning by doing and making things requires a selection of appropriate materials, which has been accumulated progressively:

- Ask students to supply everyday objects such as plastic bottles, yoghurt cartons, boxes, etc. Try to keep a supply at school.
- Consider sharing materials and equipment with the CDT department.
- Construction kits enable students to test ideas quickly.

- Allow students access to materials so that they can make selective decisions on what they use.
- Stock a range of fixing materials such as glue, tape, nails, screws, etc.

Tools and equipment

Constructive use of materials is only possible if the appropriate tools are available to manipulate them:

- Make sure students know how to use these tools and in a safety-conscious fashion.
- Offer a variety of tools, e.g. cutting, hole-making, forming and fixing implements.
- Ask students to complete equipment lists to technicians in advance of lessons.

- Make storage of tools accessible and accountable. Try tool boards with silhouetted hooks.
- Make students responsible for selecting appropriate equipment and its orderly return to the lab technician or storage space.

Working Space

The working environment is critical to facilitating constructive work. Nobody likes to work in cramped conditions or even areas which are too spacious:

- Arrange desks, benches, chairs, etc. in a manner conducive to the work.
- Mobile tables are better than fixed benches since they allow greater flexibility in the way they can be set up.

- Small groups will find planning and discussion easier around a small table; or even without a table.
- Make space available for storing part-finished models or components of long term investigations.

Practical investigative problem-solving can just as easily be conducted with existing science apparatus and materials. However, opportunities should be seized to present existing science practicals in a more open-ended way. This makes work instantly more problem-solving in its nature.

Group work

An investigative or problem-solving approach encourages students to discuss their ideas, debate pros and cons, and suggest modifications or alternatives. The student will find, therefore, that working in cooperation with peers is a considerable advantage as well as a stimulus to problem-solving. Try to vary group size according to the activity. Too small a group can cause pressures which lead to frustration, whereas too large a group can leave individuals redundant:

Examination of how groups organise themselves in order to tackle problem-solving tasks is informative. There are two basic categories:

- The 'all-in' approach, where a whole group completes one part of a task before moving, en masse, to the next.

- The division-of-labour' approach, where individuals or sections of the group take responsibility for certain parts of the task.

The division-of-labour approach can be used to encourage co-operation between groups, by apportioning different elements of a project to separate groups. Look at chapter 3, Group discussion (talking and listening) for more advice on group work.

Reporting back

Sometimes, not enough time is devoted in secondary schools to students sharing their experiences and achievements with their peers. Reporting back gives students the opportunity to present ideas and detail processes they have been through. Practical advice on reporting back and presenting work is given in chapter 6, Presentation.

Problem-solving activities from scientific investigation

Tasks which are presented as more open-ended investigations, with little or no guidance, begin to move into the realm of problem-solving. This is because we tend to associate problem-solving with overcoming a difficulty or obstacle. In some cases, the difficulty might simply be a lack of information or understanding of the method of approach. Once this is discovered the problem simply becomes a task. In other cases, the obstacle may be limited resources, cost, time, poor design, etc.

Frequently it is easy to turn an investigative task into a more open-ended and stimulating problem. It is also possible to set problems which require students to carry out one or more investigations in order to provide information to solve a problem. In this way, problem-solving becomes a more holistic function, and has a meaningful context for scientific investigation.

Many examples of scientific investigation exist in the National Curriculum Attainment Target 1. The examples can easily be set in a problem-solving context; in some cases by simply rephrasing the activity.

Example of problem-solving activity
'These crystals are not growing fast enough. Why?' (paragraph D4 (4.2))

A problem can be presented along the following lines:
You are a research chemist working for a large chemical company. The production manager needs to increase the speed at which copper sulphate crystals grow, because the process is taking too long and increasing production costs considerably. Your manager asks you to investigate the problem and come up with your recommendations.

The **objective** is clearly to speed up the rate at which the crystals grow, and make the process cost effective at the same time. The **difficulty** is that crystals grow too slowly, and keep production costs high.

ACTIVITY 11.6
Working in pairs or threes, select some examples of investigations from AT1 and rephrase them to set them in a problem-solving context. Identify the objective(s) and any possible difficulties.

Looking at investigations

Progression

The rationale for the National Curriculum is that students should develop their knowledge and understanding of science through the performance of whole investigations, i.e. an understanding of scientific procedures is developed whilst using scientific concepts that have already been experienced or acquired.

The programmes of study are not particularly helpful to those teachers who wish to produce a progression of skills and processes. They can be used only to compile a list of skills for each key stage. The statements of attainment provide greater insight into possible lines of progression. An understanding of what students should have experienced in previous key stages is more likely to produce learning activities which build upon previous experiences, i.e. students are more likely to be involved in challenging situations; a point which is frequently levelled at science departments by Her Majesty's Inspectorate.

In an investigation there are many factors which can change. These are called variables. The National Curriculum frequently refers to variables and all teachers need to be clear in their minds what the language of variables means if they are to assess process skills. If staff have difficulty with the language then page D12 of the non-statutory guidance will help. The Assessment of Performance Unit (APU) reports provide further help with this. The following example is taken from the APU database. It is an investigation to test students' performance at 11 years old:

'Find out how far the clockwork caterpillar moves when the winder is turned completely round different numbers of times. Try three different numbers of times but do not try more than six times.'

Ask yourself 'Which factor will I change systematically?' This factor is the **independent** variable. Then ask yourself 'Which factor will I judge or measure?' This factor is the **dependent** variable. Finally ask yourself 'Which factors will I keep the same throughout the investigation?' These factors are the **control** variables and make the test fair.

Teachers will not only need to be aware of the progression and variables within an investigation, but also need to gain experience at assessing the level of an investigation. The complexity of the variables decides the level to some extent, but the content also needs to be looked at. The content can be a valuable factor to help differentiate activities for students. Naturally, the content should be relevant.

ACTIVITY 11.7
Try to identify the different variables in the following investigation. Plan how you would perform the investigation, and decide what level it is at in the National Curriculum.

'Find out if Fairy Liquid washes more dishes than supermarket own-brands.'

So how does the National Curriculum's model for scientific investigation compare with a general problem-solving model?

Comparison of these two models is interesting and similarities can be seen between them. Essentially they are the same. The National Curriculum model effectively rolls a number of problem-solving stages into one. Both models provide a suitable framework for tackling problem-solving.

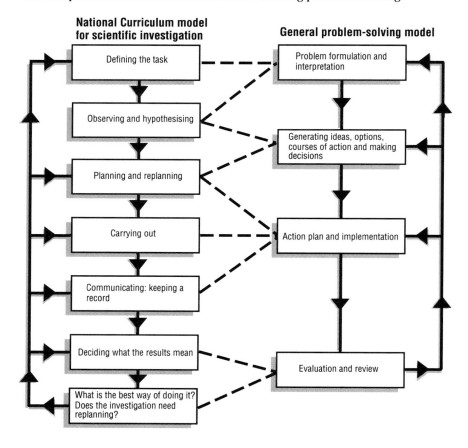

12

Video and audio tape recordings

Using educational broadcasts with colleagues

Video and audio tape recordings

Which resources should I use?

Preview and selection

Copyright for television programmes

Classroom management
- preparation for audiovisual work,
- during the broadcast,
- after the broadcast.

Duality of text

The hidden curriculum?

Making audio and video recordings in school

Practical advice

Introduction

Why use the strategy?

'I *hear* and I forget,
I *see* and I remember,
I *do* and I understand'

Although 'seeing' a television programme may well be an excellent aid to memory, this ancient Chinese proverb is a reminder that no video or audio resource should be used in isolation. Each programme needs to be preceded or followed by an active lesson. This helps students to learn and understand by doing things. The published teachers notes that accompany broadcasts provide many suggestions for these activities. Indeed, many of the strategies in this book are easily linked to the use of TV and radio in science teaching.

> **ACTIVITY 12.1**
> *Brainstorm ideas, preferably with a colleague, on the advantages of using audio and video resources in class.*

Audio and video resources can prove helpful by:

- providing experiences that can not easily be gained first hand, e.g. dangerous experiments, or interviews with eminent scientists;
- saving time, e.g. highlighting the evidence of a study which took over a year to complete;
- aiding in the collection of inaccessible data, e.g. the visual evidence collected by remote sensing satellites;
- providing special photography or enhanced sound to show details normally unintelligible to humans, e.g. time-lapse film or studies on animal communication beyond the range of our hearing frequencies;
- allowing the examination of personal or threatening experiences at a distance, perhaps through third parties seen in documentaries or dramas, e.g. sex education, or ethical/social issues;
- creating mood and atmosphere or affecting the emotions, e.g. the human consequences of environmental damage;
- providing the inspiration, motivation, or curiosity to help a student through a project;
- encouraging interest in particular areas of study, e.g. by introducing thought-provoking questions and practical problems which warrant further investigation, or outlining a problem or defining an area of study that merits further investigation;
- adding variety to topics by giving alternative viewpoints or approaches;
- reflecting back aspects of the viewers' and listeners' own lives and experiences, underlining and valuing them, e.g. individuals will find important, different aspects of the same programme or extract. Sometimes they may see and hear people who look and talk like themselves, and who may share their concepts and preoccupations, enhancing self-concept and giving them status and the courage to articulate their opinions;
- allowing students to reflect on their own lives and experiences, by identifying with people in programmes who share similar thoughts or occupations.

The cliché 'one picture is worth a thousand words' is certainly true of television. Concepts are quickly built up by the rapid intercutting of visual images and examples. The viewer soon begins to piece together ideas or associations on the material being watched. The combination of sound and pictures provides a powerful, sometimes emotional, impact.

Radio broadcasts are particularly suitable for providing up-to-the-minute information on topical science issues. Take the nuclear waste issue as an example – broadcasts deliver a range of voices and opinions through interviews with those closest to it. Programmes often raise awareness of scientific developments in society by engaging the listener in the human elements of such issues. Radio is an excellent stimulus for discussion using this technique. A programme on in-vitro fertilisation may feature an interview with a mother, and highlight the moral and ethical decisions that need to be made.

Radio also provides students with support for their own independent investigations. It is particularly good at facilitating small group or individual work in science, at the students' own pace.

Using educational broadcasts with colleagues

Both the BBC and some independent television companies broadcast programmes intended specifically for the teacher. These include INSET programmes for a particular area of the science curriculum or programmes related specifically to a series of science programmes. This type of programme can be of particular use in showing examples of active learning to colleagues, governors and teachers during in-service training days and departmental and PTA meetings. Also, extracts of programmes broadcast for students can be excellent starting points for discussion.

Some examples:
- Classroom projects shown in science series are a source of new teaching approaches.
- Recent scientific developments and information are often contained in new programmes.
- Programmes on safety techniques are useful models for future class work.

Departmental heads and primary post holders can use this material legitimately as a vehicle for curriculum discussion, for examining classroom management and for the professional development of colleagues.

Educational broadcasts can be used as starting points for discussion and explanation at parents' and governors' meetings. Because it is a 'neutral' resource the audience may be more prepared to articulate their opinions about how something could be tackled, without implying direct criticism of current school practice, or reflecting on individuals within their own organisation.

The use of audio and video resources is highlighted by the National Curriculum's emphasis on the gathering and organising of information from a variety of sources, and the use of modern communication systems.

Using the Strategy

Which resource should I use?

ACTIVITY 12.2
Find out what video and audio tape resources there are in your department. How are they stored or catalogued?

Look for resources that fit the topics or themes you are using. This means doing some prior research and being selective, e.g. using one programme rather than a whole series or using only a short extract from a programme.

Exploring audio and video stores in other departments can be a very worthwhile exercise. Often, tapes stored by one department can be utilised in another. There is a lot of overlap in the minds of resource producers in geography, science and technology, for example. A comprehensive catalogue of recorded information can be invaluable to all concerned, and can save time, too.

All independent TV or BBC school and adult education series have some form of printed support material, be it worksheets, wall charts, pamphlets or published books. There may also be computer software linked to the broadcast. Some computer packages are designed to be used interactively with video or audio resources. These challenge students with problem-solving activities.

Read the checklist of points for choosing recorded tapes:

Is it appropriate?

- Is the content suitable?
- Is it at the right ability level?
- Is the language level acceptable?
- Is the programme duration acceptable?
- Is the intended information presented well?
- Should I use short extracts or the whole programme?
- Can I edit out unwanted material easily?
- Should I show the tape more than once to bring out different layers of meaning?

Is it a summary or is it a stimulus?

- Does it only give information?
- Does it summarise work already studied?
- Does it answer specific questions?
- Is a lot of the information new?
- Does it arouse curiosity or provoke thought?
- Does it pose more questions than it answers?
- Where should I use the material: at the beginning, middle, or end of a topic?

How much teacher intervention is needed?

- Is the programme structured well enough?
- Is it very open?
- Is input needed, during and after the programme?

Obviously, any helpful advice recorded on evaluation cards would be a great help at this stage.

Organising a collection of audio and video tapes thematically, is impossible if several programmes from the same series are on one tape. Buying a box of E30 duplicating grade tape wholesale, as opposed to the equivalent duration of E240 professional grade tape from a high-street shop may prove to be the better buy, educationally. Shorter length audio cassettes have the same advantages.

Preview and selection

Many teachers make notes on teaching points and pupils responses when first viewing or listening to a tape. This takes no extra time, and if teachers can be persuaded to do this on a departmental card, the notes can be stored with the tapes for future reference. Alternatively, the notes can be stored in a box file under the title of the relevant teaching modules, thus providing a catalogue at the same time. The notes can be extended to give information about the style, pace and tone of the programme or points of particular use. In this way teachers save invaluable time previewing and cataloguing material. Comments should be kept brief and relevant to the teaching departments concerned. A record card which contains too much information may remain unused. Often the synopsis and teacher's notes supplied with a broadcast or pre-recorded tape are already very detailed.

Last, you may also wish to add details of cross-curricular links to the card or extracts that may be useful in other subject areas or topics. An interesting exercise might be to get teachers from all disciplines to do this on the next training day.

Series title: *Wonderland Science*

Length: *15 min*

Theme/subject: *Windmills/Alternative energy*

Video: ✓ Audio:

Programme title: *Power puff*

Age range: *11–13*

Date made: *1986*

Used by: *Ms Holmes* With class: *Y9*

Content: *Fits the following Y9 year course modules 2(i) 3(iv). Approach better suited to year 2.*

National Curriculum ATs and levels covered: *Useful as background information only at AT3 level 4 and AT4 levels 5, 6 and 9.*

Style: *Film extracts linked by lively presenters in studio. Oversell line of power company which features in film (bias?).*

Student response: *Boys rather bored, but girls were provoked into asking lots of questions. Wise-cracking presenters fell flat; edit out next time.*

Follow up: *Tried practical group activities 3(ii) and 8(i) in notes — excellent.*

Useful extracts: *Best parts of programme — middle section (stands on its own, 5 min in, ended about 12 min into programme) - about wind power stations (wind farms) in California. Line nos 0073-0099. Show just this bit next time.*

Related resources: *SATIS. Also computer software linked to programme (worked better than TV programme — could be used without it).*

ACTIVITY 12.3
Try making an evaluation card for a particular tape that you are currently using. In addition to general points check the tape against National Curriculum ATs and levels. Compare your card to the sample evaluation card given.

All record systems must be accessible, so where should they be kept? This, of course, will depend on individual schools. A centralised system may seem the most appropriate solution, but this can discourage regular updating of information. If a library or resource department already exists,

this may well be the most suitable point for the development of a record system. In most schools there is a strong argument for having a central **register** of recorded material, with the evaluation cards being attached to each cassette concerned.

ACTIVITY 12.4
Preview a tape recommended by a colleague with reference to the above check list.

119

Copyright (television programmes)

At the time of going to press only school broadcasts and general output designated for adult education can legally be recorded. BBC and independent TV community education officers will be able to tell you which programmes come into this category. LEAs and individual schools not covered by an LEA's licence will have to pay a licence fee in order to be allowed to record broadcast programmes, including both schools and general output programmes. It is worth automatically recording programmes if you think they may be useful. All you will have to do if they are not is recycle the tape. Failure to record could be expensive. The production company may be prepared to sell you a copy, but this can involve an individual technician duplicating a tape on a one-off basis. These costs will ultimately be passed on to you. The market prices of videos sold in the high street are often based on duplicating at least 5000 videos at a time. That is more than the total number of secondary schools in this country!

Details of the licence scheme are available from the Educational Recording Agency Ltd, 33–34 Alfred Place, London WC1E 7DP; tel (071) 255 2034.

Classroom management

Broadcasts are usually shown to whole classes or large groups. There is enormous value in students coming together in a shared experience, particularly at the start or finish of a project. Students may have pursued different lines of enquiry or had different experiences. However, whole classes may not always be the most effective units for audio-visual work. Tapes of radio broadcasts, in particular, are often more appropriately used in small groups or with individuals so that the students can stop, rewind and fast forward the tape as necessary. So as not to hinder the rest of the class students can be encouraged to wear headphones. Even if the broadcast is viewed or listened to by a whole class the activities preceding it or the follow-up work may best be organised into group work (strategies for group work are outlined in Chapter 3).

Preparation for audio-visual work

The most common preparation for audio-visual work is teachers telling students 'points to look for in the tape'. However, teacher and student judgements, interests, priorities and observations can differ, so productive work and questioning can result from differences in perception.

Give only a brief outline of the programme and then ask students to work in pairs or groups before the programme to discuss what questions and issues they expect (or would like) the tape to raise.

Teachers should prepare students well before a broadcast is played to them. The student should be allowed to plan an active approach to the material and to know what knowledge or skills they are expected to get from the broadcast. Students should be told the educational context in which the broadcast is taking place, what they are expected to do and what is going to happen afterwards. However, this does not mean that they need a detailed synopsis.

During the broadcast

Students watching television programmes, educational films or listening to the radio need tasks which focus learning. Passive note-taking is not the best solution, since much of the information can be lost if a programme is viewed (or listened to) only once. This is especially true of television programmes, since they have two texts – an audio one and a visual one. Students can easily lose visual information while writing notes on audible text.

More active learning is precipitated using the pause, still frame, or review facilities of a recorder system:

- This gives students time to answer questions; or work through activities without missing what follows.
- This allows students to summarise what has already been seen (or heard), and predict what will follow.
- This allows whole-class discussion of issues and group discussion (groups can reassemble before continuing with the broadcast).
- This makes reflection and analysis easier.
- This enables teachers to comment on particular points in the programme.
- Students can review difficult sections of the programme.
- Students can ask questions whilst the tape is stopped.
- Invite students to supply their own commentaries or describe particular frames.
- Ask if the broadcasted commentary is valid (do students recognise more visual points if the sound is turned off?)
- Is the selection of images biased or prejudiced in any way?

Student ownership of the learning is further enhanced if they are allowed to control the stopping, reviewing or forwarding of the recorded tape.

ACTIVITY 12.5
View a tape and consider ways you can encourage active learning while showing it. Make notes on your strategies, e.g. questions you might pose, points at which to pause the tape.

After the broadcast

Follow-up work after watching a video, or hearing a radio programme is important. Try to avoid questioning whole classes on points requiring only factual recall. Nurture more open-ended responses instead, giving students the opportunity to express their own opinions, experiences and understanding in relations to the broadcast. Open recall allows very personal responses to be made:

- Ask students to list ideas, statements or issues derived from the programme in their own order of importance.
- Ask which three images or statements students remember most and why.
- Ask if there are any questions the students would like to address to one another, the people in the programme, the people who made the programme, or the teacher.
- Return to a still frame, picture or sequence of text, and discuss with students what went on before and after.
- Try role plays based on the issues and people in the broadcast.
- If factual recall must be used, ask students to design their own questionnnaires.
- Give students sequencing exercises to help clarify their ideas.
- Use active practicals to follow up and bring out the ideas in the broadcast.

In the teacher's notes often supplied with recorded material, look first at those recommended follow-up suggestions that will encourage genuine first-hand active practical enquiry for individual and group work.

ACTIVITY 12.6
Think about the last time you used a recorded tape in the classroom. What active follow-up work could you support it with.

Students can be invited to supply their own commentaries or describe a particular frame; if the commentary is too easy or simplistic what has been left out? When the sound track is off what extra details do they begin to notice? Is the broadcaster's interpretation of this visual evidence valid, or are there alternatives? Is the selection of images biased or prejudiced?

Duality of text

Sometimes the pictures and commentary are in conflict with one another; the commentary may be explaining the benefits of traditional farming methods in stopping soil erosion, but the images of poverty in the Third World may be giving students a different message. Traditional farming methods may look very unattractive compared with 'hi-tech' methods. Unless the follow-up strategies are open, active and encourage participation this might not be obvious to the teacher who is expecting the students to be giving more weight to the spoken text, and some of the more subtle arguments will not be explored.

ACTIVITY 12.7
Examine a video tape for duality of text. What alternative responses might your students give? How can you use these?

The hidden curriculum?

Graham Sellors who produces an infant science series *All Year Round* has his own checklist:

- How does the programme maker see the viewer (what is the role of the learner) – active participant or passive recipient?
- Is the programme material child-centred – does it stem from or relate to children's interests and experiences?
- Who does the talking? Who is in the authority position?
- Do the programmes reflect the kind of society we live in – a plural society?
- How are women/men, girls/boys portrayed? Are traditional role stereotypes reinforced or challenged?
- Does the programme recognise that emotion is an important factor in education?
- Does the programme encourage concentration on the process rather than the product (does it see the method as more important than a 'body of knowledge') or does it reinforce the 'narrative transmission' mode of teaching?
- Are the programme material/concepts/language appropriate for the intended audience?
- Are there instances of ambiguity?
- Does it encourage the children to ask questions?
- Who is the programme for – the teachers or the children?
- Will the viewers enjoy it?

Overall, what effect do the programmes have on the children's concepts of themselves as learners? Do they encourage the children to see themselves as central to a process which is about them and to which they can contribute (are the programmes concerned with learning) or do they portray children as 'having something done to them' (being taught)?

ACTIVITY 12.8
What hidden curriculum can you find in your tape? How can you use this or counterbalance it?

Making audio and video recordings in school

The use of audio visual aids in school can be taken one step further by allowing students to make their own radio bulletins or video films. This is particularly active, and might be used for the following:

- to record a field trip or industrial visit;
- to record the stages in setting up an experiment;
- to produce a 'green' advert for the whole school;
- to record project work.

Students enjoy these types of activities, and with careful planning they are able to learn or apply scientific knowledge and concepts. Reading, writing and group discussion skills are also developed during the process.

It is important to seek cooperation between departments, so that there is no content overload in trying to deliver the National Curriculum.

Before beginning any audio or video tape-recording session, there are two important points you should tackle:

- Establish a structure for the programme, and have a clear outline of content. Pinpoint the beginning, end and linking stages of the recording. For video work it is important to get the pictures to complement the commentary. Remember that even documentaries have a strong narrative structure and story line. Consider which statements will advance or clarify the programme, and which serve only to distract the listener.
- Decide on whose perspective the story will be told. For example, the student view on a field trip will be different to that of the teachers, but even so will make an interesting form of presentation.

Practical advice

Video filming

- Avoid too much use of the zoom lens together with panning. This will make the viewer 'sea-sick'.
- Begin and end all panning shots with a still picture. This makes any necessary edits easier.
- Zooming from a close up to a wider shot is usually more interesting than the reverse.
- Vary your shots.
- If filming people talking, use head and shoulder shots to cut out any gesticulating hands.
- Reserve head only shots for emotional impact.
- Storyboarding should be practised. At the very least design a shooting script. Storyboards are made up of a series of simple drawings which show each shot or scene which is to be included in the film. By planning a logical sequence of shots in this manner (or by preparing a simple shooting script) heavy editing of the film is avoided, this being especially important if editing facilities are unavailable.
- Don't overload commentary – let pictures speak for themselves.

- If access to sound dubbing equipment is possible, make full use of its benefits, e.g. people talking over moving pictures is far more interesting than viewing the two separately.
- Don't shy away from extra 'takes'.
- Take some close-up shots when filming long sequences of slow or repetitive actions. When the film is edited a short close-up can be used to replace a longer piece of action. Such edits are called **cut-aways**. For example, in a film showing glassblowing, short-duration close-ups of the blower's hands or face can be used to replace longer-duration shots of the actual blowing process. Enough of the long shots should be used, however, to illustrate clearly each stage in the production process.
- If you are filming indoors, always have windows to your back, otherwise shots will look dark.
- Do not film the same shot too long – professionals work to 5 seconds!
- Be aware that microphones attached to the video camera can be multidirectional and pick up unwanted sound such as the deep breathing of the camera operator.

Audio recordings

- Students can be encouraged to use such recordings for a variety of activities such as: gathering evidence (e.g. noise surveys); recording progress; interviewing their fellows; and making final reports.
- Without editing facilities the use of audiotape by students needs careful planning but can be a valuable tool in small group work.

What educational television and radio material is available?

For any teacher to gain maximum benefit from audio and video work, it is essential to know all the resources currently available in educational programming. Often, valuable material is missed, either because its existence is not known, or teachers cannot trace the relevant producers. We hope the following information will ease these difficulties:

Education officers

Both the BBC and some independent television companies have education officers who are able to inform schools of available programmes.

BBC education officer

Telephone (081) 752 4396/7 and ask to speak to the Education Officer (Science) for information in connection with science programmes. If there is a local officer based in your area he or she will also be able to help.

BBC Education (telephone (081) 991 8031) will have sent you an annual programme booklet, a subject leaflet and a programme timetable. If you have not received this, or can't find it, request another copy.

Independent television education officers

Education officers for the independent television companies can inform you of their current resources, advise you on specific needs, and help with INSET. They are currently regionally based and may be able to visit.

At the end of the franchise period in 1993, arrangements for contacting the Education Officer in connection with series commissioned by and broadcast on Channel 4 will change. Details of how to contact these new Education Officers will be published in both the annual literature and in the series notes. The current local ITV offices are listed below. When the new series start being broadcast on Channel 4, schools should contact Channel 4 direct as a first stage. Channel 4 are at 60 Charlotte Street, London W1P 2AX, telephone 071-631 4444.

Publications about schools broadcasts

ITV Schools also publish an annual programme booklet, science subject leaflet, timetable and primary and middle school topic chart which, along with the similar BBC material, are essential for planning science into a curriculum. Telephone your regional independent television company if you can't find them.

The *Radio Times* and *TV Times* give listings of all TV programmes, *TV Times* gives a detailed supplement of schools broadcasts at the beginning of each term.

Pre-recorded videos

Pre-recorded videos of series for schools and general output programming are available for purchase from a number of sources, such as BBC Enterprises (telephone (081) 576 2361), Central TV Video Resource Unit (telephone (021) 643 9898), Academy Television, formerly Yorkshire TV Enterprises (telephone (0532) 43825). Other independent television companies have arrangements with commercial distributors. For these you will have to contact the education officer of the company which produced the series.

Company resources

Companies such as Shell, ICI, British Nuclear Fuels, BP and British Gas produce much educational and publicity material, including video and audio tapes. Find out whether your school already has any of this material and, if so, where it is stored. Look for advertisements in the TES, Education Guardian, etc., and write for catalogues of such material.

Open University

Many of the programmes produced for the Open University Science Foundation Course S102 contain useful excerpts for secondary school science. You will need to find the times of the broadcasts (from the *Radio Times* and *TV Times*) and also to check that your school or authority has permission to record these.

Commercial Film and Video Distributors

Educational specialist distributors often send catalogues to schools, teachers' centres, local libraries and resource centres who stock them.

13
Games and simulations

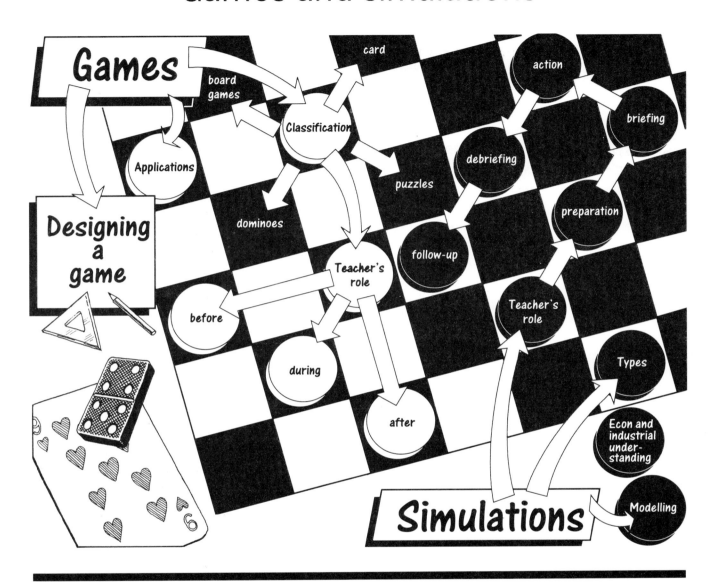

Introduction: games

What are games?

There are many definitions of the word game. For the purpose of this
chapter we refer to a game as being an activity which requires one or more
players, has rules and is competitive. To be classified as a science game the
activity must involve the use of scientific skills, knowledge or processes.

Why use scientific games?

In recent years there has been a dramatic increase in the use of games in
the classroom. Their use, however, as an integral part of the science
curriculum, has not been fully explored by many teachers. The positive

effects that games can have on attitudes can only be channelled towards more effective learning if this is understood. Games offer students the following:

- excitement,
- competition,
- reality,
- participation,
- enjoyment,
- motivation.

Any game used to develop scientific learning **must** involve appropriate decision-making. If a game does not incorporate this process, it runs the risk of becoming mechanical, and student learning is severely restricted.

ACTIVITY 13.1
Brainstorm the skills you think scientific games can help develop.

Many skills can be developed while playing educational games. These will obviously depend on the type of game, but we suggest the following skills can be realised:

- problem-solving,
- communication,
- reading,
- listening,
- cooperative,
- manipulative.

But how do games help students to learn about science? The answer is simple:

- Games increase enjoyment, commitment and enthusiasm. The competitive edge, if handled sensibly, can motivate students. This includes bright under-achievers, and students with learning difficulties.
- Games encourage group relationships. The atmosphere of friendly cooperation (or competition) both between and within groups, creates an excellent learning environment.
- Students are actively engaged in their own learning, which is highly interactive and student-centred.
- Student-teacher interactions are improved upon.
- Reinforcement and retention of facts is on a par with more traditional teaching methods. Concentration span is extended due to the motivational nature of games.

- Games form excellent revision aids. Students spend more time on revision if it is made interesting and enjoyable.
- Games can simplify complex concepts, and thereby make them easier to understand.
- Feedback to the teacher is very direct. A teacher can observe a student's performance closely by joining in a game. This less formal 'assessment' can be completed in a more relaxed atmosphere, and give a more reliable indication of student comprehension.
- Games can be accommodated in single or double lessons.
- Games are a useful camouflage under which to explore sophisticated scientific concepts with younger or lower ability students.

How do I acquire games?

Two important sources of games are teachers and students. Although producing games can be more time consuming than using ready-made materials, the process of design can be a stimulating one. It also allows the creation of games to suit individual classroom situations.

Commercial games which are ready to use, can be obtained from a number of publishers and manufacturers of educational material.

What type of games can be used?

A detailed review of the types of games available is undertaken later in the chapter, but it is true to say that almost any game can be adapted for use in science lessons. The main categories seem to be board games, card games, domino-type games and puzzles. Computer games are dealt with in chapter 8, Information Technology.

Are games just for the end of term?

No! We cannot stress this enough. The use of games for end-of-term entertainment, or lesson-fillers, completely undermines the educational value of this strategy. Games are potentially a powerful learning aid and should be integrated with the syllabus.

Using the strategy (games)

Applications

There are four important points to remember when games are used to convey scientific knowledge or skills:

- Games are not a panacea – they should be combined with other teaching techniques.
- Games should not be used in isolation – they should be carefully incorporated into a course.

- Games should not be over-used – this can be boring and counter-productive. (Games form effective summaries at the end of a topic, rather than introductory material.)
- Games must be followed-up – they are not just for fun. (Inform students that the teacher will check what they learn from a game.)

> **ACTIVITY 13.2**
> *List some examples of how games can improve learning environment.*

The following statements are intended to indicate how games can be used:

Reinforcement and revision
Reinforcement and revision activities are made more intresting and less repetitious if games are introduced. Student involvement is increased, and concentration is enhanced.

Teaching facts, skills and concepts
Games aid the assimilation and simplification of difficult concepts.

Special needs
Games increase concentration and motivation, and lengthen the attention span. Try the student copymaster, States of matter, on page 220. Give verbal assistance if it is required.

Bright under-achievers
The competition and excitement of a game can motivate under-achievers. The renewed interest can spread to other aspects of science.

Non-streamed groups

In mixed ability groups games can be used to provide extension work and support material, and to encourage students of different abilities to work together. The introduction of an element of chance allows less able students to win games. However, it is still essential to include an element of scientific knowledge, process or decision-making.

Independent learning

Games can be used as an alternative activity in a resource-based learning model. With a choice of games differentiation can be written into the model.

Inaccessible practical work

Games can take the place of dangerous experiments or industrial processes that cannot be done in the school laboratory.

Basis for a lesson or topic

Games can form a basis of a lesson or topic. They provide an interesting and stimulating way of introducing a topic or concept.

Extra-curricular work

Games are suitable resource materials for science clubs and can also form interesting homework, e.g. patience, or crosswords.

Economic and industrial understanding

Games can model industrial processes.

Classification of games

Games can be split into four main groups: board games, card games, dominoes and puzzles.

Board games

Board games are usually associated with moving counters around a board; moves being dictated by the throw of a die. Such games are often modelled on the likes of Ludo, Snakes and Ladders or Monopoly.

Board games are especially suited to processes that are cyclical. The water cycle is an example of a cyclic process, and if a board game were based on it, counters could be moved around the various stages of the cycle. Information or rules which relate directly to the processes involved in the circulation of water can be designed. The use of chance cards will give an added dimension.

Card games

Card games are reasonably easy to devise. Once designed, the teacher can either provide students with ready-made cards, or get students to make the cards themselves. The most common models for scientific card games are Happy Families, Snap, and Whist. Scientific properties can be matched to groups of elements for example.

Card games are well suited to classification activities, in which cards can be physically collected and sorted into groups according to chosen criteria, e.g. vertebrae, metals, electromagnetic waves. These games often require greater existing knowledge of science than board games, but by their very nature some acquisition of knowledge takes place.

Dominoes

The matching of one half of a domino with the appropriate half of another is an activity most students are familiar with. Games of this nature are therefore particularly suitable for students with learning difficulties. Domino-type games are ideal for matching pairs of objects, organisms or stages in a process. For example, dominoes can be made so that an animal and a habitat have to be matched. The level of the game can be controlled according to the complexity of information given and the rules applied. Extension work for more able students can be distributed in this way.

Dominoes are useful at the end of a topic for summary or revision work, once information has been assimilated. There is an example of a domino-type activity in the student copymasters (see page 220).

Puzzles

The recent avalanche of puzzles appearing in comics and magazines read by children makes it sensible to capitalise on this increased awareness and enthusiasm. There are numerous types of puzzles. Anagrams, wordsearches and crosswords (see page 218) all help with building scientific vocabulary. Matching games, odd-one-out, jigsaws (see page 186) and coding games all help with sorting and classification.

Puzzles have a variety of uses and can be tackled at a number of ability levels. Puzzles can be introduced at a variety of stages in a work scheme. For example:

- as a stimulus to lesson-work,
- as a means of covering a topic,
- to support video activities,
- an extension material,
- for summary work and revision.

A word of **warning**: puzzles can all too easily become straight-forward mechanical exercises. This is especially true of wordsearch activities. It is important that students have to **do something** with the words collected. This 'sting-in-the-tail' philosophy should be adopted with **all** puzzles. The following lists a few suggestions:

- words found in a wordsearch can be used to label a diagram or write a report,
- unravelled anagrams can be entered into an incomplete table, or half-labelled diagram,
- jigsaws can be labelled once they are completed, or used as a basis to write an experimental report.

The teacher's role

While games are being played the teacher's involvement can vary considerably and will depend on the type of game being played. Whilst it is important to let the students work things out for themselves as much as possible, it should be clear **why** they are playing the game, **what** science is involved and **what** the rules of the game are. The teacher's input is vital, and it is critical that follow-up work is undertaken.

Essentially there are three, equally important, stages to be considered when attempting a game in the classroom.

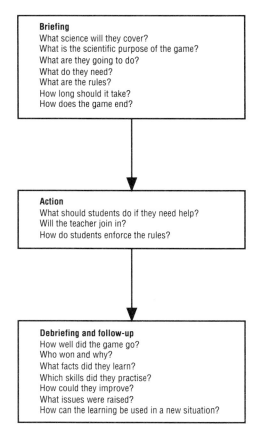

Briefing
What science will they cover?
What is the scientific purpose of the game?
What are they going to do?
What do they need?
What are the rules?
How long should it take?
How does the game end?

Action
What should students do if they need help?
Will the teacher join in?
How do students enforce the rules?

Debriefing and follow-up
How well did the game go?
Who won and why?
What facts did they learn?
Which skills did they practise?
How could they improve?
What issues were raised?
How can the learning be used in a new situation?

Before the game (the briefing)

Teacher's notes

- Make sure you are fully conversant with the rules of game and how to set it up.
- Collect all necessary resources together beforehand.
- Introduce a game and describe it. This is especially important if there are complicated rules or if prerequisite knowledge or skills are needed.
- Decide whether to join in a game. This can be done as a player (encouraging student-teacher relationships and a relaxed atmosphere) or as a coordinator or questioner.

During play (the action)

Teacher's notes

- Whenever possible take on a supporting, co-ordinating and managerial role. Try to leave the games to the students. (Games are intended to be student-centred.)
- If necessary step in to solve problems and explain points, possibly acting as the final arbitrator.
- Control the timing of the activity.

After the game (the debriefing)

Teacher's notes

- Supervise checking and packing away of all components of the game by the students.
- Start the debriefing as soon as possible. New experience and knowledge need to be discussed and shared so that students are aware of the scientific content in a game, and see that learning has taken place.
- Consider testing students after a game to see what knowledge or skills they have learned. Puzzles can be used for this purpose, rather than a traditional written test. This or other appropriate follow-up work is extremely crucial to the educational value of game-play.

Designing a game

If a game is going to be designed the following points should be borne in mind:

- What type of game will it be?
- What science will be covered?
- What will be the level of interaction? Individual? Group? Class?
- What materials can be used?
- Can an existing game be modified?
- How many players will there be?
- How long will the game take?
- Will the game be noisy?
- What sort of follow-up work can be done?

Students can be encouraged to design their own games. The task forms an interesting problem-solving exercise at the end of a topic. For example, after a topic on magnetism ask students to design and construct a game that uses a magnet. Students are familiar with commercial magnetic games and will apply their knowledge imaginatively. Similarly, ask students to review (or revise) a topic by getting them to design a puzzle on it. The results can be tried out on other students within the class. Factual information is reviewed twice in this way – once when the puzzle is designed, and once when students attempt a puzzle designed by a colleague.

The motivation for designing a game can be increased if a judging system is introduced. The panel of judges may consist of students, teachers or visitors to the school. Parents, governors and industrialists can also get involved. Games designed by students form impressive displays at open days and parents evenings!

Be warned!

- Check whether similar games are already being used in other parts of the school. Over usage of certain types of game can jeopardise their educational value.
- Limit the amount of time spent playing games. They are only stimulating if used occasionally. Link games to the most suitable points in the curriculum.

- To reiterate a point made earlier, make sure games are not just mechanical exercises, which students can follow without applying scientific knowledge or making decisions.
- Chance cards or dice introduce an element of luck into a game. Although a useful tool when encouraging special needs or lower ability students, the better games restrict the chance element, and rely on knowledge and skills to enhance player progress.

Introduction: simulations

What is simulation?

Simulation activities involve students working as realistically as possible within a reproduced situation. Information is supplied which allows students to operate within the simulation. The students are not role playing. Role play can be described as 'person-centred' in that issues and concepts are explored by asking students to imagine they are in someone else's shoes. Simulations are 'job-centred' as the emphasis is on carrying out a certain task. Students behave according to the task in hand, with no teacher intervention.

Why use simulation technique?

ACTIVITY 13.3
Brainstorm your ideas on the benefits of using simulations.

Simulation provides a framework and philosophy in which students are not only active participants, but have full responsibility (and authority) for their actions and decisions. The technique encourages a cooperative approach, provides a creative atmosphere and develops problem-solving and communication skills, as well as knowledge and understanding of scientific concepts.

The main benefits of simulation work are summarised by the flow diagram:

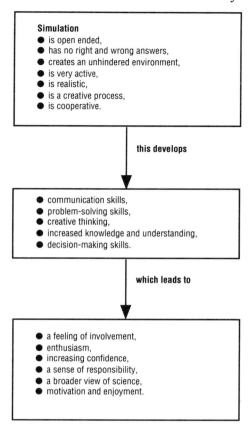

Simulation also allows teachers more time to observe and assess students. Because students are in control of the work and determine its outcome, a teacher is free to view the actions externally.

Does simulation take up too much time?

There is no doubt that simulation technique will often take more time to prepare and carry out than more traditional teaching methods. However, this is balanced by the many benefits which grow from the enthusiasm simulations help to create. Simulations, as with many other active learning strategies, become less time consuming with practice. Their appeal is greater if they are regarded as ways of teaching the curriculum, rather than as 'add-on' luxuries.

Can all students cope with simulation?

With its emphasis on active learning, cooperation and reality, simulation technique is well suited to cater for students of all abilities. The open-ended nature of the strategy allows more gifted students to expand ideas, whilst those with learning difficulties find the cooperative nature of the activities less threatening. The variety of ways in which information is given or received allows a shift in emphasis away from reading and writing skills.

Using the strategy (simulations)

Types of simulation

There are many kinds of simulation. These include:

- problem-solving,
- computer,
- models,
- radio/television debates,
- newsroom,
- boardroom,
- research team,
- medical.

A wide range of situations can be created to cover scientific information and issues in a stimulating way. The stages of simulation are similar to that of a game. The flowchart outlines these.

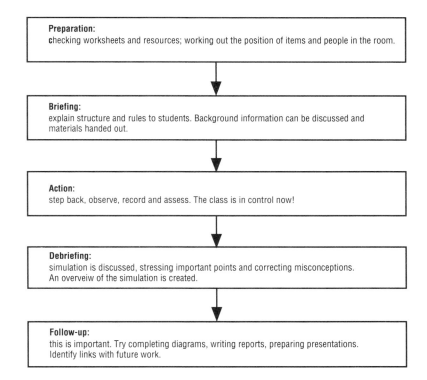

Preparation:
checking worksheets and resources; working out the position of items and people in the room.

Briefing:
explain structure and rules to students. Background information can be discussed and materials handed out.

Action:
step back, observe, record and assess. The class is in control now!

Debriefing:
simulation is discussed, stressing important points and correcting misconceptions. An overveiw of the simulation is created.

Follow-up:
this is important. Try completing diagrams, writing reports, preparing presentations. Identify links with future work.

The teacher's role

Simulation technique places the teacher in many different roles and those experienced in operating the strategy stress that this is one of its attractions. During the preparation stage the skills needed are very familiar to science teachers. Planning and preparing for a simulation is similar to planning and preparing for practical work. Success is more likely if there has been rigorous attention to detail.

The briefing role, although it draws on many diverse skills, is a familiar one. Teachers are well versed at giving information to students and explaining rules. This does not necessarily have to be conveyed in a lecture or written on to a blackboard. We urge teachers to use some of the more active strategies discussed in this book.

The action stage is probably the least familiar to teachers, and as such may be viewed with some reservation. Statements such as 'they are in control now' and 'the outcome is in their hands' indicate a move towards anarchy in the minds of some teaching staff. However, nothing could be further from the truth. The teacher's role only involves stepping back, not stepping out! Common experience shows that students are so interested in the simulation that the problem of control does not usually arise. To maintain involvement the teacher can take on the role of an observer and recorder, noting down points which need to be raised during the debriefing. Assessment can also be carried out here. Obviously, as with any new teaching strategy, a fairly simple example needs to be selected to begin with. Support strategies for simulation work, such as group work, DARTS activities and methods of reporting back, are all discussed in this book.

Preparation

Teacher's notes

- Run through the simulation mentally. Discuss it with a group of colleagues if you can.
- Check you have all materials to hand and position them where they are needed.
- Make copies of notes or information students may need, e.g. notes on running and simulation, or important data.
- Arrange documents around the room for easy circulation.
- Make name/function tags for participants, e.g. ion and electrode badges (see the student copymaster, Electrolysis, on page 219).

- Arrange furniture to suit the simulation. Consider a change of venue if this is not possible.
- Decide how to allocate roles and functions. Random selection is often adequate, but it is important to have a cooperative atmosphere. This may require some selective allocation of roles.

Briefing

Teacher's notes

- If students have not done simulation before, explain the nature of the strategy. Emphasise that students will make all decisions during simulation and you cannot offer advice (unless acting as a consultant).
- Explain any background information. Make the briefing active! Try DARTS, puzzles, or plays.
- Outline the structure of the simulation, and any mechanistic rules.

- Outline the duration of events and tasks.
- Hand out notes to participants and clarify general points.
- Allocate roles or functions.
- Distribute role cards, and name/function tags.
- Decide whether further briefing may be required, e.g. for specialised tasks in the simulation.

Action

Teacher's notes

- Allow participants autonomy.
- Unless you have a role disengage yourself from the activity.
- Do not be tempted to guide or advise.
- Take the opportunity to observe and assess.

- Make notes on common misconceptions and questions to discuss in the debriefing.
- Remember! This is an open-ended activity – students learn from their mistakes.

Debriefing

Teacher's notes

- This stage should really be a continuation of the action.
- Ask students to remain in their action groups and present any findings or problems that arose (and how they tackled them).
- Ask participants to explain their functions, in turn. This will give all students a general overview of the simulation, and enable them to build up a picture of the model and how it works.
- Be positive in your summing up!

Follow-up

Teacher's notes

- Assess student comprehension of the simulation and the knowledge they gain.
- Make this stage active. Arrange tasks which require completion of processes or filling in diagrams, for example.
- Simulations can be followed by presentations, debates, letter writing, or producing articles for imaginary newspapers and magazines.
- Make explicit links to future work and consider the value of the simulation in this respect.

ACTIVITY 13.4
Working in a small group, try to sketch out ideas for a simulation activity which will provide a model for a scientific process of your choice.

The debriefing and follow-up stages make further demands on the communication and presentation skills of the student. They may require help or support with this. Use the advice give in the chapter on presentation.

Now that you have read all the advice on simulation, try the student copymaster, Electrolysis, on page 219, or have a go at the following activity.

A short note about economic and industrial understanding

Economic and industrial understanding is one of five cross-curricular themes identified by the National Curriculum Council. It is clear that science has an important contribution to make in this area.

The nature of simulation make it a very powerful tool for developing an awareness of economic and industrial aspects in an active and interesting way. A glance back at the simulations listed on page 135 will illustrate how many are set in industrial and commercial settings. Further examples of how simulation can be used to develop understanding in these areas can be found in publications produced by the Centre for Alternative Teaching Strategies in Biotechnology, at Sheffield University. Examples include *Mini-fermenter and vinegar production* and *The resistance scandal.*

Modelling

Modelling is a powerful technique that allows abstract scientific principles to be studied in a more concrete way. Many of the processes that students are introduced to within the science curriculum cannot be observed or measured directly. Students never see the structure of an atom, heat energy moving through metals or enzymes breaking down food substances, yet we expect them to understand and recall how these things occur.

In order to aid both understanding and retention, models offer the opportunity for students to study representations of processes on a larger scale. This is especially important for students with learning difficulties. Not only does modelling allow visualisation, but in the case of three-dimensional models, it also allows 'hands-on' experience. This tactile use of models, especially if linked to sorting and/or decision-making tasks, is an important technique. Computer models and two-dimensional paper exercises are equally useful.

An example of modelling, Enzyme action – lock and key hypothesis, is included in the student copymasters (see page 222). The model allows students to visualise the way active sites on enzymes can only be occupied by specific chemicals, and helps them to appreciate why enzymes only catalyse certain reactions.

Models can be used as props during group discussion or as centrepieces for presentations. Moving, working models are especially useful, and can be designed by students as part of the learning sequence.

14

Assessment

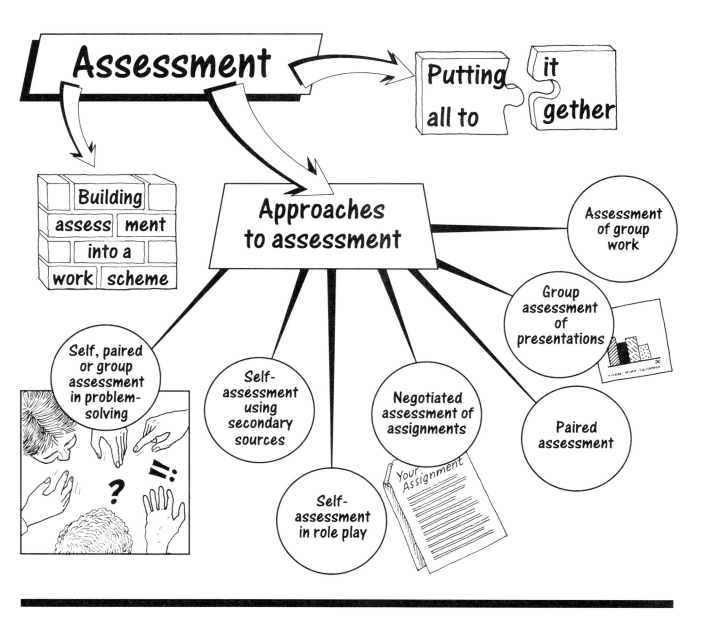

Introduction

Why use the strategy?

The question you might be asking yourself is – having decided to adopt active teaching and learning approaches in science lessons, can I still assess student attainment and satisfy the needs of the National Curriculum? You may also be wondering whether these approaches can assist the development and assessment of personal, social and study skills, to enable an holistic picture of the student to be built up. The answer is yes! If we take a broad view of the purposes of assessment, as set out in the TGAT report, and implicit in the Record of Achievement development, we can begin to see how this is possible. The TGAT report states that assessment should be formative, diagnostic, summative and evaluative.

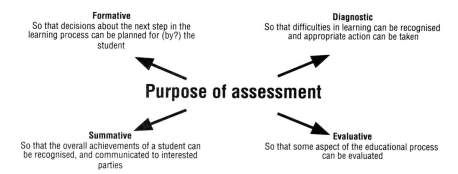

Purpose of assessment

Formative
So that decisions about the next step in the learning process can be planned for (by?) the student

Diagnostic
So that difficulties in learning can be recognised and appropriate action can be taken

Summative
So that the overall achievements of a student can be recognised, and communicated to interested parties

Evaluative
So that some aspect of the educational process can be evaluated

The formative and diagnostic purposes fit comfortably with the aims and practices of active learning. Active learning is a student-centred process, with heavy emphasis on what the student, rather than the teacher, is doing. Any assessment, with a formative (or diagnostic) purpose must be student-centred. It must involve processes and give rise to information useful to individual students and aid their progress or development. It follows then that if students are active and increasingly responsible for their own learning, they should also be actively involved in their own assessment, with corresponding further increase in responsibility.

Using the strategy

The National Curriculum has forced teachers to adopt a much more systematic approach to assessment. Assessment opportunities, methods and recording systems need to be planned alongside the schemes of work devised to deliver the programmes of study. The National Curriculum is defined in a way that leaves decisions about teaching and learning approaches largely in the hands of the teachers themselves. We argue that the adoption of more active approaches allows teachers to enlist the help of students in this complex, but worthwhile, assessment process.

The planning process could follow the pattern set out here:

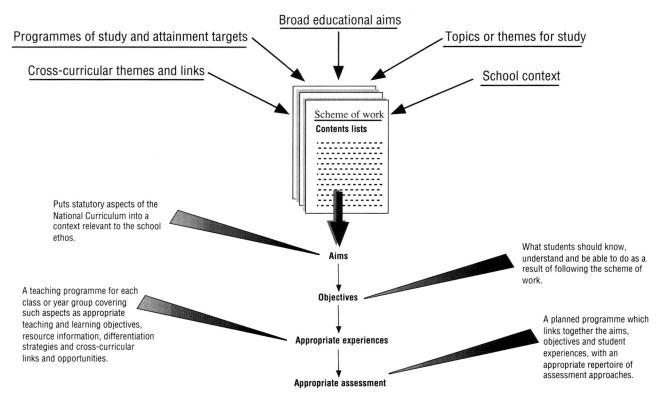

Broad educational aims

Programmes of study and attainment targets

Topics or themes for study

Cross-curricular themes and links

School context

Scheme of work
Contents lists

Puts statutory aspects of the National Curriculum into a context relevant to the school ethos.

Aims

What students should know, understand and be able to do as a result of following the scheme of work.

A teaching programme for each class or year group covering such aspects as appropriate teaching and learning objectives, resource information, differentiation strategies and cross-curricular links and opportunities.

Objectives

Appropriate experiences

A planned programme which links together the aims, objectives and student experiences, with an appropriate repertoire of assessment approaches.

Appropriate assessment

The rest of this chapter looks at aspects of assessment suitable for schemes of work including active learning. GCSE-style practical and course-work assessment is already described in a wide variety of published material, and so this is not repeated here.

Building assessment into a work scheme

In order to plan an assessment strategy for a module, a number of questions must be answered:

- What National Curriculum statements of attainment does the module provide opportunities to assess?
- What other qualities can be assessed throughout the module (e.g. presentation skills, group work)?
- What will the balance be between assessment during teaching and set-piece assessment?
- What will the balance be between assessment carried out on the basis of what the students produce (product assessment) and assessment of what students actually do (process assessment)?
- To what extent will students be involved in assessment?

The answers to these questions will depend upon the topic being covered, the range of teaching approaches adopted, and the general philosophy of the individual, department or school. Within the context of this book it can be assumed that whatever external pressures help mould the assessment strategy, students will be involved at the heart of the process. There will also be planned opportunities within the module for product and process assessment both of statements of attainment and of other course objectives. What follows is a series of suggestions for approaches to assessment which are appropriate to student active science.

Approaches to assessment

The following principles should be applied, bearing in mind the four assessment purposes listed by the TGAT report:

- Students should understand the process and the purpose of the assessment.
- The assessment strategy should be appropriate to the curriculum objectives.
- The assessment approach should not interfere with the learning process, but should as much as possible be integrated with it.
- Assessment should provide for all levels of achievement within your student population.
- Assessment should concentrate on the positive aspects of the students' abilities, attainments and qualities.
- Students should be given the opportunity to reflect on the work they do and pass judgement on themselves.

The following approaches are covered by the remainder of this chapter:

- self-assessment using secondary sources;
- self-assessment in role play;
- negotiated assessment of assignments;
- paired assessment;
- group assessment of presentations;
- assessment of group work;

- assessment of group work by teacher observation;
- self, paired and group assessment in problem solving.

The assessment approaches covered here are not meant to exhaust all possibilities, but represent those suitable for use with active learning. It is assumed that these strategies will run hand-in-hand with other, more traditional, assessment activities.

Self, paired or group assessment in problem-solving

In Blue Crystal Ltd (page 214) students are asked to solve a problem concerned with dissolving copper sulphate in water. Students have to design a way to speed up the process, in an industrial simulation. During the planning and carrying out stages of the activity the students could be asked to complete a planning process sheet. This could be completed during and straight after the activity. It would allow the students to reflect on their performance, either singly, in pairs or as a group. The teacher would have a written record of some of the decisions the students made, providing an insight into the problem-solving process they carried out. (N.B. It is not necessary to include all four sections of questions each time.)

These are planning process sheets for use in problem-solving activities:

1 The problem

What is the problem and what are you trying to achieve?

Why is there a problem in the first place?

What are all the different things that the problem depends on and what do you need to find out about them?

What information and materials are available to help you solve it?

2 Planning ideas

What ideas or designs have you got for solving the problem?

What are all the different things that could be changed or tested?

What might happen if you followed each idea or design?

Which course of action seems most promising and how will you decide on this?

3 Planning and investigating

What is your chosen plan?

What equipment or information is needed? What is available?

What is your checklist or schedule for carrying out your plan? How will you control your investigation?

What will you need to record, and how?

4 Checking the results and methods

What do the results tell you?

Does your solution match what you set out to do? Could it be better and, if so, how?

Did you follow the plan and did your group work well together?

Do you need to try another idea or design?

Self-assessment using secondary sources

Self-assessment is useful during and after activities on researching information from secondary sources since it fosters the development of personal and study skills. Students are often responsible for managing both time and resources, and need to make decisions about the nature of material available to them. A high level of autonomy is allowed. A short series of questions allowing students to reflect on their learning can be devised as follows:

Self-assessment in role play

Role play is one of the most difficult learning approaches to assess. The value of role play is easily lost if the teacher is doing an assessment while watching. Students would almost certainly 'clam up' if they thought someone was observing them with a clipboard, ticking boxes. It is far better if the students do their own assessment:

Self-assessment in role play

When you have finished the role-playing activity think about these questions. Write down your answers if you wish.

- *Was it difficult to 'get into role'?*
- *How did you feel in your role?*
- *What did you learn?*
- *What was your favourite part of the activity?*
- *What could you do to improve your ability in role playing?*
- *What surprised you about the discussion during the role play?*

- *Did you change your mind during the discussion?*
- *What are your real (out-of-role) opinions on the subject?*
- *How has the activity made you feel about the issue now?*
- *Do you want to find out more about it?*
- *What will you do now?*

Students can consider the questions prior to a group or class discussion. This allows the learning processes which occur during the role play to be evaluated. This evaluation is vital if students are to assimilate any new knowledge and understanding from the activity. It will offer the teacher a chance to consider, first, how effective it was in achieving the objectives of the session and, second, what comes next for individuals, groups or the whole class.

Negotiated assessment of assignments

Students can be involved in negotiating assessment criteria. Before individuals, groups or whole classes begin an assignment, they can set the criteria for the subsequent assessment. With individuals, this can be done on the basis of one-to-one discussion, and can revolve around improvement of certain aspects of work. The setting of individual targets and action planning are features of many Record of Achievement schemes. Action plans may be built into the module record sheet, or be separate to it. An example is seen below:

Many other points can be written into an action plan.

The whole class could be involved in setting joint learning targets and agreeing the assessment criteria. First, individuals or pairs could be asked to consider 'What makes a good investigation report' (or project, or a solution to a specific problem-solving activity). The students could then be grouped into fours or fives, and asked to produce a list of, say, four criteria for assessment. In a plenary session the teacher could then list the main criteria on an OHT or board as they are suggested by each group. As each idea is put forward, it could be used as a discussion point by the teacher and class. Alternatively, the list could be written with no discussion, and then gone through afterwards to establish a final checklist.

The students could then use the criteria to check their own progress during and after the assignment. This can be done as individual or group assessment. The following shows the type of sheet which can be prepared to record assessment.

Self assessment – Projects, reports and assignments

We agree what makes a good *PROJECT*

How did I do

1
2
3
4
5
6

What was good about my work?

How can I improve it?

How will I do this?

Paired assessment

Students often work 1n pairs, particularly when they are doing practical work. The special relationship which develops during paired work can be a powerful tool in assessment. Paired assessment can be used in almost all situations already described, with minor changes in the language of the questions. Here are two other examples of general assessment approaches more suited to paired assessment:

Paired assessment: prompt sheet

Talk about points 1, 2 and 3 with your partner before the assignment.
Talk about the other points after the assignment.

1 Discuss with your partner what you have to do.
2 Discuss any points you do not understand and try to explain them to each other.
3 Are there any resources or information you need to carry out the assignment?
4 How successful were you in completing the assignment?
5 What part of the assignment did you do best?
6 What part of the assignment do you think you could do better?
7 Were there any parts of the assignment which were easier to do because you were part of a pair?
8 What did you learn?
9 What was your favourite part?
10 What have you learnt that will help you with your next assignment?
11 Did you work well together?

The card below shows how GCSE assessment criteria can be incorporated into a paired assessment. The criteria can be drawn from those listed in the syllabuses, or redrawn by the teacher to match the particular activity being assessed. The example given is for drawing a graph, which could be assessed as part of Strand (iii) of Sc1.

Paired assessment: graph check list   Name _____   Class _____

The graph has:

☐　　　the correct title

☐　　　a correct label on each axis

☐　　　correct units on each axis

☐　　　points or bars drawn in the right place

☐　　　a line drawn in the right place (for line graphs only)

My comment about the appearance of your graph:

　　　　　　　　　　　　　　　　　　　　Signed _____   Date _____

Group assessment of presentations

Students should be given the opportunity to outline their ideas to peers, teachers and parents presentation. This could be as a result of:

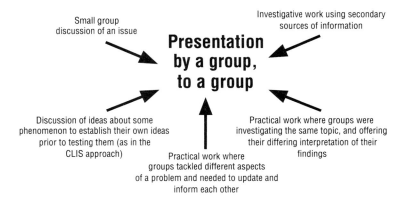

The activity **Presentation** can be used by students to plan their own presentation and, from then on, be used as a group self-assessment exercise each time a presentation is planned. The actual event could be assessed by the class using the method outlined above in the section on **Negotiated assessment of assignments**. Following the assessment, a group presentation certificate could be issued to the group:

Group presentation

Topic: Class: Date:

The following aspects of   Group members:
presentation were assessed
by the class:

1　Interest   Assessment:
2　Information content
3　Coverage of AT2
4　Language used
5　Quality of visual aids
6　Group work

A group presentation questionnaire can be used. Members of the class fill in the questionnaire, and return it to the group doing the presentation.

Group presentation questionnaire

Group presentation topic:

How did the group get your attention in the topic? How did the group hold your interest? __ __ __ __ __ __ __ __ __ __ __ __ __ __ __

Describe one thing about the presentation which you thought was imaginative. __ __ __ __ __ __ __ __ __ __ __ __ __ __ __

List four things you learnt as a result of the presentation. __ __ __ __ __ __ __ __ __ __ __ __ __ __ __ __

Make one suggestion which would help the group improve their next presentation. __ __ __ __ __ __ __ __ __ __ __ __ __ __

What will you do as a result of seeing the presentation? __ __ __ __ __ __ __ __ __ __ __ __ __ __ __ __

Assessment of group work

The assessment of group work covers a host of different processes, ranging from assessment of group activities by students, through the assessment of an individual's contribution to group work by the teacher. Many of the approaches already discussed can be used by groups to assess their own work, with only slight changes in the language.

For a major collaborative project, it is often best to establish a division of labour before beginning. If each group member's responsibilities are sorted out at the start it may reduce friction during the actual activity. Groups can draw up a short contract, to ease progress during the project. The following figure gives a possible outline:

Group work contract

Group members:

What we want to achieve:

Group responsibilities and tasks		
Group member	Responsibilities and tasks	When by?

We will finish the activity by: __ __ __ __ __ __ __ __ __ __ __ __ __ __ __

How we will present our work: __ __ __ __ __ __ __ __ __ __ __ __ __ __ __

How we will assess our work: __ __ __ __ __ __ __ __ __ __ __ __ __ __

Groups can be given a progress report to complete during the project. This will help them to evaluate group processes as well as project work. Here is an example of such a report:

Group work progress report

In your group take 10 minutes to think about the following questions. You do not need to write anything down.

- How much of the work have you finished so far?
- What work have you not done yet?
- Is everyone doing their fair share?
- Do you need to change anything to finish the work (times, responsibilities, overall objectives)?
- What help do you need to finish the work?
- How will you get this help?
- How do you feel working in this group?
- What have you learnt so far?
- What are you going to do next, as a group, and as individuals?

Allocating marks to group members

There may be occasions when you need to allocate marks to individual members of a group, based on the performance of a group assignment or project. You may have decided that marks out of 10 or percentages are a way in which you can communicate to students about overall progress, or performance in particular tasks. What do you do if a group of four students collaborates on a piece of work or activity? How can you give each one a mark?

One suggestion is that if four students carry out an assignment (perhaps having agreed between themselves beforehand such things as the division of labour and assessment criteria – see the Group work contract), then the group can be given a number of marks to share out amongst themselves. Following a presentation of the findings in a project, you may say to the group that out of a possible top mark of 40, they have a total of 36 to share out amongst themselves. They would then have to discuss the issue amongst the group and allocate the marks accordingly.

Assessment of group work by teacher observation

Perhaps the most difficult aspect of group work concerns the assessment of individuals by the teacher. The teacher will obviously have access to the products of the group work (reports, assignments, presentations, etc.), but the contribution by each member to each aspect of the work may be difficult to ascertain. This will be harder in terms of the assessment of academic progress, and marginally less so in terms of personal, social and study skills. Regular monitoring of the various group and self-assessment activities can help here. The following list clarifies when it is possible to assess individual contributions to group projects:

- Group work with one major product, such as a presentation, report or model will be difficult to assess at individual level. Individual learning may need to be assessed by some other method, such as end-of-module tests, questioning individuals or individual written work.
- If a group activity ends in individual work, such as a test, assignment or report then learning may be assessed easily at individual level. If true group work has occurred the individual assessment outcomes will act as an evaluation of that aspect of group work.

Individual learning is relatively simple to assess if the project involves distinct contributions by individuals.

Observation is an important part of the teacher's repertoire for finding out what is going on in the classroom. This is very obvious but it needs stating. If we want to know what is going on we must look and listen. However, if we want to refine the process so that it gives us specific information then we have to consider more closely the role of looking and listening. Classroom assessment involving teacher observation will be more efficient and we will learn more about what it is that is going on if we are guided by questions to which we seek answers. This implies we know why we are observing, and what specific information we are trying to collect.

The reasons for observation are likely to fall into one or more of these categories:

- to assess knowledge and understanding;
- to assess group interactions;
- to assess communication skills;
- to evaluate the effectiveness of a particular aspect of the lesson;
- to provide a basis for support, guidance or intervention in group work.

We need to make sure we know why we are observing group work. It is likely to be as simple as: 'I will observe this group involved in the ATLAS activity Blue Crystals Ltd to see if the individuals are working productively,' or 'I am going to observe this group discussing their interpretation of the results to the activity to assess the level of their understanding.'

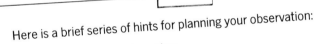

Here is a brief series of hints for planning your observation:

- Know why you are observing.
- Know what you are looking for.
- Plan your checklist.
- Plan who you are going to observe and for how long.
- Don't allocate all the lesson for the activity. You will need time between groups or individuals for recording information.
- Don't try to observe everything. Good checklist design will help to focus your thoughts, but don't be restricted by this if some other notable occurrence takes place.

Putting it all together

Many suggestions have been made about approaches to assessment, beyond the traditional methods we use, particularly for pre-1989 GCSE. It might be said that if anyone attempted to use all those listed in this chapter, as well as those others not mentioned here and necessary for external examination purposes, then all we would be doing is assessing. However, this would be to ignore the increased role we have given to the student in the process. Giving responsibility to the students wherever possible will ease the burden the teacher bears. In addition, many approaches suggested can be seen as truly formative, in that the questions students are being asked are mainly to assist in the learning process, not to gather information for summative purposes. This is what is described in the TGAT report in its list of the four chief purposes for assessment. We will recall that these are: formative, diagnostic, evaluative and summative. Hopefully, using a wide range of teaching and learning styles, coupled with a wide repertoire of assessment methods, we will satisfy the TGAT criteria more easily than with a narrow range, which is more suited merely to provide a summative judgement after the learning event than able to reflect, mould and enhance it. A module record sheet where active assessment has been planned for a series of student activities is shown.

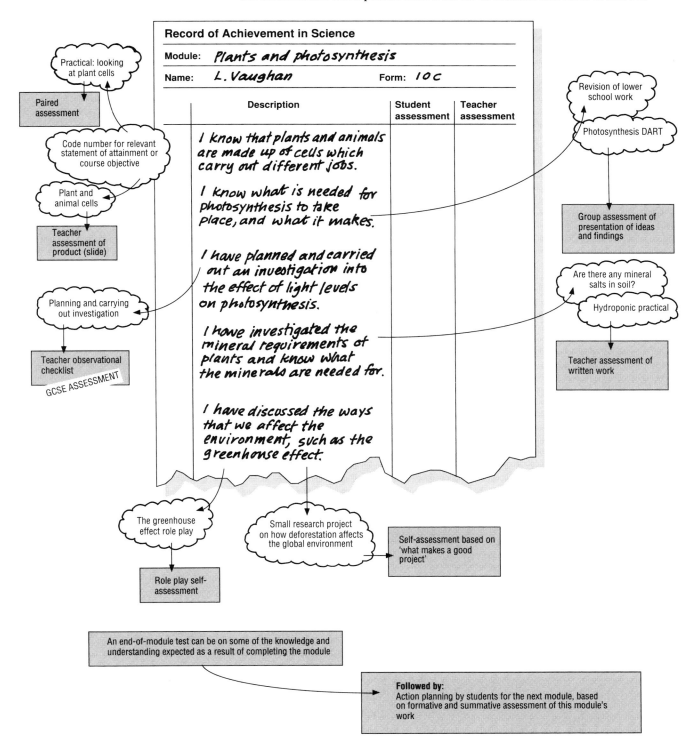

Record of Achievement in Science

Module: *Plants and photosynthesis*

Name: *L. Vaughan*   Form: *10 C*

Description	Student assessment	Teacher assessment
I know that plants and animals are made up of cells which carry out different jobs.		
I know what is needed for photosynthesis to take place, and what it makes.		
I have planned and carried out an investigation into the effect of light levels on photosynthesis.		
I have investigated the mineral requirements of plants and know what the minerals are needed for.		
I have discussed the ways that we affect the environment, such as the greenhouse effect.		

Practical: looking at plant cells

Paired assessment

Code number for relevant statement of attainment or course objective

Plant and animal cells

Teacher assessment of product (slide)

Planning and carrying out investigation

Teacher observational checklist

GCSE ASSESSMENT

Revision of lower school work

Photosynthesis DART

Group assessment of presentation of ideas and findings

Are there any mineral salts in soil?

Hydroponic practical

Teacher assessment of written work

The greenhouse effect role play

Small research project on how deforestation affects the global environment

Self-assessment based on 'what makes a good project'

Role play self-assessment

An end-of-module test can be on some of the knowledge and understanding expected as a result of completing the module

Followed by:
Action planning by students for the next module, based on formative and summative assessment of this module's work

15

Controversial issues

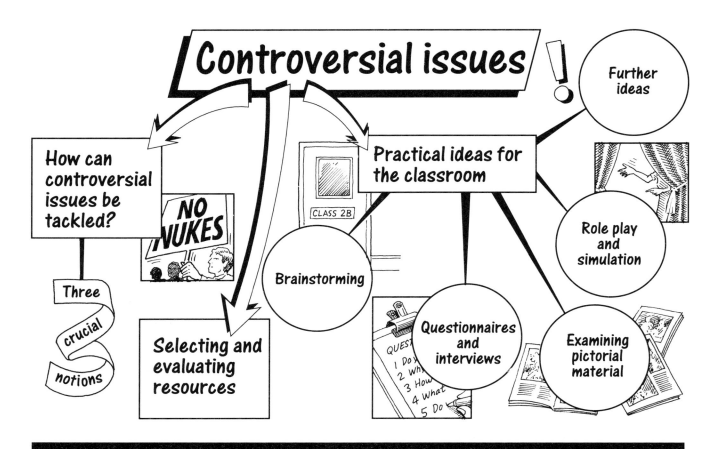

Controversial issues

How can controversial issues be tackled?

Three crucial notions

Selecting and evaluating resources

Brainstorming

Practical ideas for the classroom

Questionnaires and interviews

Examining pictorial material

Role play and simulation

Further ideas

Introduction

What is a controversial issue?

A controversial issue involves value judgements and cannot be settled by fact, evidence or experiment alone. To be truly controversial should be considered important by an appreciable number of people.

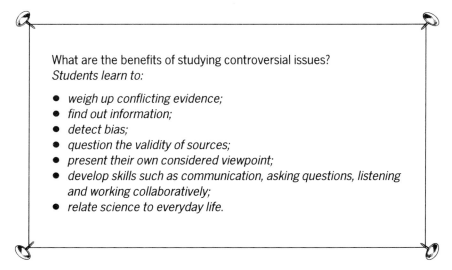

What are the benefits of studying controversial issues?
Students learn to:

- *weigh up conflicting evidence;*
- *find out information;*
- *detect bias;*
- *question the validity of sources;*
- *present their own considered viewpoint;*
- *develop skills such as communication, asking questions, listening and working collaboratively;*
- *relate science to everyday life.*

What do we need to consider when teaching controversial issues?

Teachers need to give a balanced viewpoint:

- All views are expressed with equal emphasis and given the same time and space.
- The necessary scientific principles needed to understand the issue are explained.
- Arguments, opinions and information from all sides are presented.
- Sensitivity and tolerance to different views are encouraged.
- Bias, prejudice and indoctrination are excluded.
- A neutral stance is maintained.

Why use active learning strategies with controversial issues?

Highlighting awareness and deepening understanding of controversial issues undoubtedly benefits from the active participation of the student. The teacher can use a wide range of active learning strategies to help students assimilate knowledge, explore and exchange views, and examine attitudes.

Why include controversial issues in the curriculum?

> **ACTIVITY 15.1**
> *Carry out a survey of the National Curriculum for science programmes of study to identify those topics which are likely to include controversial subjects.*

Rather than seeking to justify the inclusion of controversial issues in the curriculum, it is interesting to see what valuable science is lost if these ideas are excluded. A wide cross-section of scientific knowledge falls within the bounds of controversial study areas, such as smoking, alcohol consumption, dieting, pollution, farming and tourism.

The National Curriculum for science emphasises the importance of the application and economic, social and technical implications of science, giving ample opportunity for the introduction and discussion of controversial issues in this area.

An education which ignores controversial issues is arguably inadequate. The decision not to study issues of this nature, not only neglects the scientific knowledge surrounding an issue, but it also ignores the learning processes associated with their debate.

Such a narrow treatment is also likely to omit historical context and give students a false impression of a subject. It is argued that science teachers are often guilty of misrepresentation of subjects, often presenting them as unproblematic, value-free and non-controversial.

The above justifications are content based. In other words, the inclusion of controversial issues is justified in terms of the content of the material which is presented to students. An equally convincing justification can be based on the skills and processes which students can learn by examining controversies. Students can learn to weigh up evidence, to search for information, to detect bias, to question the validity of sources and to present their own considered viewpoint. The skills of communication, listening, working collaboratively and co-operating in group sessions can all be enhanced. Clearly the development of these skills will depend on the approach of the teacher.

This argument is supported if we consider the curriculum from two perspectives: horizontal and vertical. Look closely at the figure:

The vertical curriculum

Skills and awareness \ Subjects	Maths	English	Science	Humanities	Modern languages	Design and technology	Physical education
Language skills							→
Problem-solving skills							→
Life and social skills							→
Information skills							→
Communication skills							→
Information technology awareness							→
Multi-cultural							→
Skill in handling controversial issues							→

The horizontal curriculum

ACTIVITY 15.2
Study the figure closely. Do you think that there are other skills in the curriculum that are not illustrated? How will the 'cross-curricular' dimensions of the National Curriculum fit into this pattern?

ACTIVITY 15.3
The inclusion of controversial issues can be justified in terms of content or skills and processes. Hold a group discussion with some colleagues on this.

The curriculum is often seen in terms of its subjects or 'forms of knowledge'. These form the basis of most secondary school curricula. However, it is often valuable to view the curriculum in horizontal or cross-curricular terms. The ability to handle controversial issues is just one of the cross-curricular skills which forms a justifiable component of the school curriculum, along with the other seven shown.

Using the strategy

How can controversial issues be tackled?

Three crucial notions

Three crucial notions are often employed when discussing the correct approach to teaching controversial issues. They are objectivity, neutrality and balance.

The key question in discussing the handling of controversial issues is this: to what extent should teachers act as an authority in the classroom? This question is especially difficult for teachers who are handling matters of value as well as fact.

A teacher will be able to settle disputes on factual points involved in controversial issues. For example, in a discussion on nuclear energy, a teacher can usefully correct the mistaken belief that a nuclear reactor could explode like an atomic bomb in the event of an accident. But should the teacher act as 'an authority' in settling matters of value? Clearly, a teacher who did so would not be acting objectively, neutrally or in a balanced way. So should teachers confine themselves solely to matters of fact and avoid questions of value? The suggestion rests on the belief that there is always a clear distinction between fact and value – a distinction which is questionable.

The criterion of objectivity is extremely difficult to apply in handling issues which involve a mixture of facts, values, value-laden facts, and values dependent upon people's perceptions of facts. What could possibly constitute an objective viewpoint in such cases? How can a teacher be objective when handling a discussion on complex controversial issues, except perhaps by acting as an objective authority in advising on the occasional clear-cut matters of fact?

Neutrality or balance?

The two other notions to consider are the procedural principles of **neutrality** and **balance**.

The Humanities Curriculum Project (HCP) gave the following useful guidelines on pedagogy for discussion of a controversial issue:

- Teachers should not use their authority as teachers as a platform for promoting their own views.
- The mode of enquiry in controversial areas should have discussion rather than instruction as its core.
- Discussion should protect divergence of view among participants.
- The teacher as chairperson of a discussion should have responsibility for quality and standards in learning.

These guidelines are embodied in the notion of procedural neutrality, central to the HCP, and suggest that a teacher should act as an impartial chairperson in debates of controversial topics. The guidelines are very useful, but arguably the principle of neutrality cannot fully be maintained in a discussion on controversial subjects. Take the nuclear issue as an example. In many cases the provision of information, and even direct instruction, is central to a thorough treatment of the nuclear issue. It cannot be maintained that information and instruction are always value free, since so many 'facts' come from either one 'side' or the other, but it is necessary to deliver these so that an informed judgement can be reached. An informed value judgement is surely more educational than just a value judgement, 'gut feeling' or intuitive decision. The aim of education is surely to provide students with the ability to make informed evaluations. Ignorance may be bliss, but it is anathema in education.

Other objections to neutrality as a teaching principle exist. First, a small, but potentially confusing point in the classroom, is the ambiguity of the word 'neutral'. If a neutral standpoint is taken in a nuclear debate, it is itself a positive decision, based on a viewpoint. Indeed, the concept of neutrality in relation to nuclear weapons is usually associated with the political left-wing.

Second, in classroom discussion teachers frequently encounter two problems:

- There is often no divergence of view among participants, or the divergence is not equally distributed.
- Some important viewpoints are not expressed at all.

Is the teacher therefore under obligation to present missing viewpoints or support minority viewpoints more strongly? Playing devil's advocate may be necessary to maintain a balanced discussion. However, this then runs contrary to the principle of neutrality! Which has overriding importance: balance or neutrality?

Evaluating classroom resources

One of the key problems of teaching controversial issues is that of selecting and evaluating appropriate resources from those available. Many of these resources are sent free to teachers, and suffer from one major problem: they are frequently unreadable. A lot of leaflets and pamphlets are as difficult to comprehend as legal documents. Add to this the over-complicated explanations and you have a recipe for classroom confusion.

Three other points need to be borne in mind by a teacher evaluating material. They are bias, accuracy and how dated the material is:

- The development of an ability to detect bias is perhaps one of the main aims or justifications for studying controversial issues. Most people agree that students should be able to detect bias in a wide range of media. Students must assess leaflets, books, television programmes, newspapers, etc. This is not an easy aim to achieve. The notion of bias is a difficult one. From which standpoint should bias be judged? Is there some acceptable 'centre of gravity' from which views or resources from either side can be evaluated? In short, does bias lie in the eye of the beholder, or can it be judged objectively? The problem of bias will face teachers both in discussions and in evaluating teaching resources.
- An equally difficult quality to achieve in a teaching resource – and also to judge – is that of 'accuracy'. In presenting scientific principles, strict accuracy sometimes needs to be sacrificed for the sake of simplicity or readability. A full accurate, technical account of, for example, a nuclear explosion is neither accessible nor relevant to a debate on the nuclear issue.

  Another problem in the nuclear debate is that many 'facts' are in conflict. Exactly how many missiles the USA possesses, and of what strength, is treated as a matter of opinion rather than a matter of fact. Similarly, there are conflicting data on other nuclear arsenals, on the countries capable of making nuclear weapons, on the effects of nuclear explosions and on the hazards of radiation. The boundary between fact and opinion is never sharp.
- The third criterion in evaluating resources is how dated they have become. New situations and developments regularly arise which render previous knowledge and thinking obsolete. Consider these points from the past concerning the nuclear issue: the proposed Strategic Defence

ACTIVITY 15.4
What difficulties present themselves in detecting bias in classroom materials on controversial issues? Discuss this with a colleague if possible.

ACTIVITY 15.5
Can you cite any examples of materials on controversial issues in science which are either:
- *inaccurate,*
- *dated,*
- *or biased?*

Initiative (or 'Star Wars' programme) in the USA, and the theory that a nuclear winter would result from a number of nuclear explosions. Both appeared in the media somewhat suddenly in the 1980s, and both affected people's thinking about the concept of deterrence in a fundamental way.

Below is a summary of six sets of criteria which can be used in evaluating classroom resources, for use in handling controversial issues:

Use and organisation
How will you use the material in the classroom? (Whole-class discussion, small-group work, pairs . . .?)

Students' reactions
How did the students react to it? Were they stimulated by it? Were they kept active?

Activities
What activities were students involved in? (Individual written work, writing in pairs, talk and discussion, role play . . .?)

Level
Was the level of the material suitable for the students involved? Were the reading level and the conceptual level suitable? If not, for whom would the level be more appropriate?

Bias
From what source did the materials come? Are they very obviously biased, or more subtly biased? Would it be acceptable to use them with school students?

Accuracy
Are the materials accurate? When were they published? What original sources, if any, are referred to?

ACTIVITY 15.6
Look closely at the above summary. Discuss with colleagues whether any points can be added.

Practical ideas for the classroom

Simply asking (or expecting) students to read material on a controversial issue, and then discuss it, may not be appropriate in many classes. More active learning and involvement is often needed. The following activities offer a range of alternatives:

- brainstorming,
- questionnaires,
- interviews,
- examining photographic or other illustrative material,
- role play and simulation,
- full debate with speakers and chairperson,
- active reading for learning, e.g. DARTS,
- active writing.

Of course, additional teaching resources such as film, slides and video are often available, and these will provide welcome alternatives to the written and spoken word.

All of these activities have been discussed in previous chapters, but they are considered here in the context of teaching controversial issues.

Brainstorming

Brainstorming (see page 32) is useful for starting open thinking on a new topic. This is likely to work best in a small group. It is an effective way of gathering people's ideas, associations and impressions of almost any topic. It will be most illuminating before discussion or teaching has begun.

Brainstorming a controversial issue

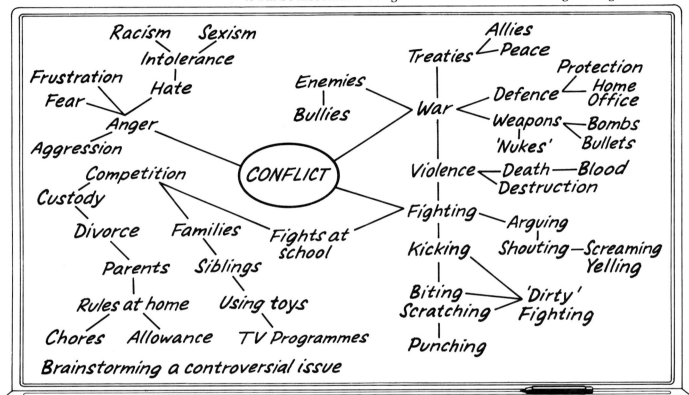

Brainstorming a controversial issue

ACTIVITY 15.7
Study the brainstorm above. Which ideas come up most often? Which feelings most obvious?

An open, non-evaluative session of this kind can form an excellent starting point for three main reasons:

- Interest and awareness are aroused.
- The teacher is provided with useful information on the views and prior knowledge of the students.
- People learn the attitudes and impressions of others in an enjoyable and non-argumentative way.

With larger or less manageable groups, individuals can be asked to write down the first three words or ideas that come into their mind in response to a given word. (This can be done individually or in small groups.) The responses can be collected and made into a large chart for display.

Brainstorming is not a new idea and it may not work well for every teacher with all classes, but it is a good way of making an unbiased, open-minded start to a topic.

Questionnaires

Another way of arousing interest is to ask members of a group to interview each other. This can be done in small groups or pairs. Interviewers can ask about peers' views, attitudes and opinions; about anxieties or worries; or even about their existing knowledge of a subject. Results can remain anonymous, and prove as interesting to the teacher as to the group members themselves. The results may be collected and displayed. Teachers may wish to devise their own interviews to suit particular classes or, better still, ask the students to make up their own interviews to try out on the others.

Questionnaires can also be used to raise consciousness and explore areas similar to those described for interviewing.

The questionnaires can be handed out to each student in the class, and once they are complete the results can be collated to form a 'class profile'. Histograms or pie-charts can be designed to display people's opinions and attitudes visually. Simple computer databases are ideal for collating and displaying results.

Examining pictorial material

Photographs, illustrations, projected slides or OHTs can all be used as alternatives to written material for generating discussion and presenting evidence. Old photographs, newspaper cartoons or topical pictures can be used to start a discussion or instigate written work.

To start discussion the teacher can:

- Invite general comments from anyone in the group.
- Focus on particular aspects of a picture, e.g. people's expressions, the likely time of the photograph, size and scale.
- Ask for impressions or associations conjured up by the picture (rather like brainstorming).
- Invite speculation on why the picture was made: What point it is trying to make? Why was a cartoon drawn?
- Invite discussion on what individuals might be saying or thinking.

Similar ploys can be used to promote written work. Students can be asked to write down three words or ideas which spring to mind when they see a picture. Alternatively, students can write down what the characters in a picture might be saying, perhaps incorporating this into a comic strip. The suggested speeches can be compared and discussed.

These, and other ploys, are all valuable starting points for using pictorial material to stimulate discussion and written work.

Role play and simulation

Controversial issues are ideally suited to role play and simulation. The actual classroom practice will depend on the style, inventiveness and imagination of the teacher. See Chapters 7 and 13 on the use of role play and simulation. Active reading and writing techniques can also help students come to terms with the wide-range of information presented in connection with controversial issues. See Chapters 4 and 5.

Further ideas

1 Looking at language

A specific activity, which in itself should lead to active reading for learning, is to look at the language used in controversial issues. Particular words can be studied. Here is another example from the nuclear issue. A list of words used to name nuclear missiles could be made – naming words such as Tomahawk, Trident, Titan, Lance and Minuteman. How do these compare with less attractive labels such as SS–4, SS–5 or SS–20? Is there any purpose in using carefully chosen names? How do these names compare with those used by the car industry: Cavalier, Sierra, Jaguar, Fiesta, Astra? What images do different names conjure up? Obviously, the car industry uses names to suggest comfort, masculinity, speed or relaxation. How important are names, and their images, in any controversial issue?

2 The statements game

One way of getting students to write about issues and then discuss them is to ask students to make short written statements on small cards. Some suggestions from the nuclear issue are: 'I wish nuclear weapons had never been invented'; 'The UK should get rid of its own nuclear weapons'; and 'Without our own nuclear weapons other countries would invade this country'. Once the statements have been written on separate cards, different activities can be followed up in class. Read the notes on the statement game on page 64.

Alternatively, instead of students' statements on an issue, points made in leaflets and publications can be used.

3 Newspaper studies

Another activity to encourage reading and writing is to examine media coverage and controversial issues from different sources, for example editorials and cartoons. Wall displays and collages could be made showing both the quantity and quality of newspaper coverage, and in some cases those of magazine articles. Different newspapers could be compared. If possible, old newspapers, or copies of parts of them, could be used to show coverage of present and past incidents, e.g. newspaper reports of the Hiroshima bomb.

All the activities described here in 1, 2, and 3 are all fairly simple, and can easily be adopted and adapted by class teachers for their own use. These, and similar ideas, have been used by teachers in active tutorial work on a variety of topics. One other example you might try is the technique described on page 64, in the section How things are, and how things should be.

To conclude

The ideas presented in this section are all offered as alternatives to a straightforward 'read and discuss' approach, which has its place but people may soon tire of. The value in many of the activities suggested is that the existing knowledge and prior attitudes of the group can be revealed, sometimes anonymously. This feedback is as essential to a teacher dealing with a contentious issue as it is in teaching other aspects of the curriculum, e.g. scientific concepts. In short, the teacher can start from where students are, both in their previous information and existing attitudes and use active learning strategies to go forward effectively.

Suggestions for further reading can be found in the bibliography.

16

INSET activities

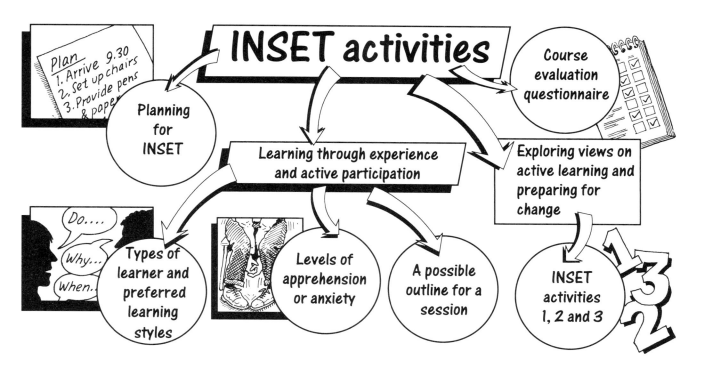

Introduction

Why use INSET?

The short answer to this is because many science teachers say so. Understandably, teachers who have only limited experience of running active teaching techniques, such as small-group discussion, role play and presentations, will want to find out more before introducing them into their classroom. There are several reasons why teachers may feel apprehensive about active teaching and learning, and these are highlighted in Chapter 1, together with suggestions for overcoming them. Other teachers who have already used active learning with some success may want to enhance their existing skills in a particular technique. We hope that this manual proves valuable to both sets of teachers. However, we do recognise that INSET work will help to support the ideas and advice given in this manual, and will no doubt complement it.

This chapter is aimed at anyone who has responsibility for providing INSET or initial teacher training, including teachers, advisory teachers and heads of department. It is not possible to cover all the active learning strategies within this one chapter, so we have limited it to three aspects:

- planning for INSET;
- running an INSET session which involves active participation and learning from experience; and
- exploring views on active learning and preparing for change.

The information and advice given here should be used in conjunction with the material given in other chapters. This will enable INSET organisers to develop sessions which deal with particular active learning strategies.

Using the strategy

Planning for INSET

If INSET is to be school-based the following questions will be helpful for planning the work:

Questions to ask yourself concerning school-centred INSET:

- Is the department/school ready for active learning?
- Does everyone know what active learning means? Is there a corporate view?
- Are you willing to work with other departments (science and other subjects)?
- Who will help with INSET (senior management team, advisory teachers)?
- How will preparation for INSET be done?

- Will it be done with individuals, pairs or groups?
- How will you extend ownership of INSET to others? Will you set tasks to challenge and extend existing teaching methods?
- How (and when) will you evaluate participants' feelings concerning INSET?
- How can you support individuals involved in the new learning in a non-threatening manner?

If INSET is being provided by an external body, a number of additional questions need raising. Naturally, many of those points concerning school-based INSET will still apply.

The following flowchart for planning INSET may prove helpful:

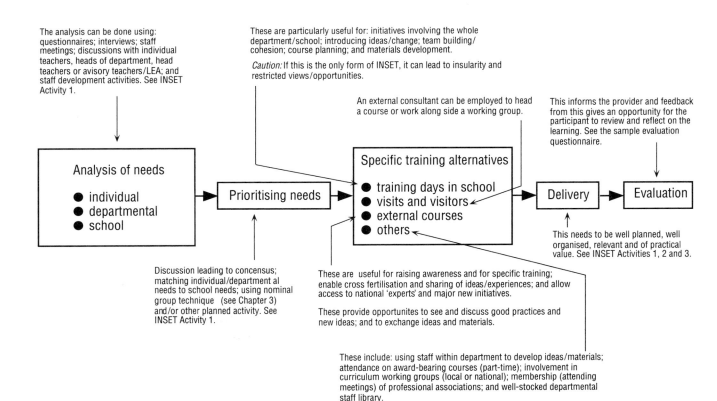

The analysis can be done using: questionnaires; interviews; staff meetings; discussions with individual teachers, heads of department, head teachers or avisory teachers/LEA; and staff development activities. See INSET Activity 1.

These are particularly useful for: initiatives involving the whole department/school; introducing ideas/change; team building/cohesion; course planning; and materials development.

Caution: If this is the only form of INSET, it can lead to insularity and restricted views/opportunities.

An external consultant can be employed to head a course or work along side a working group.

This informs the provider and feedback from this gives an opportunity for the participant to review and reflect on the learning. See the sample evaluation questionnaire.

Analysis of needs
- individual
- departmental
- school

Prioritising needs

Specific training alternatives
- training days in school
- visits and visitors
- external courses
- others

Delivery

Evaluation

Discussion leading to concensus; matching individual/department al needs to school needs; using nominal group technique (see Chapter 3) and/or other planned activity. See INSET Activity 1.

These are useful for raising awareness and for specific training; enable cross fertilisation and sharing of ideas/experiences; and allow access to national 'experts' and major new initiatives.

These provide opportunites to see and discuss good practices and new ideas; and to exchange ideas and materials.

This needs to be well planned, well organised, relevant and of practical value. See INSET Activities 1, 2 and 3.

These include: using staff within department to develop ideas/materials; attendance on award-bearing courses (part-time); involvement in curriculum working groups (local or national); membership (attending meetings) of professional associations; and well-stocked departmental staff library.

Important points for providers of INSET courses outside school:

- Who will attend the INSET training? What are their roles within the school or department?
- What is the current awareness or experience of the participants in active learning?
- What is the participant's awareness of course organisation and methodology, and of active participation (if it is expected)?

- Are the participants expected to bring along departmental information, examples of resources, etc?
- Are participants expected to complete a course-evaluation questionnaire?
- Do participants need to be made aware of any follow-up work?

Most of this information can be communicated through pre-course documentation which includes a brief questionnaire to be returned before the course starts.

Learning through experience and active participation

Teaching and learning by example are almost certain to be central features of any INSET session dealing with the theme of active learning. It would verge on the hypocritical to run such a session without giving the participants the opportunity to experience the processes at first hand, i.e. 'don't tell me – show me, involve me!'

Running a session which involves active participation can be a very rewarding experience, both for the participants and for the tutor. However, it does require careful planning and an awareness of those factors which contribute to its success and those which can cause problems.

Types of learner and preferred learning styles

It is important to be aware that in most groups there are essentially four types of learners, each having a preferred learning style. These have been identified as follows:

Type of learner	Preferred learning style
Activist	<ul><li>new experiences</li><li>active participation</li><li>'in at the deep end' challenges</li></ul>
Reflector	<ul><li>stand back and observe</li><li>review the learning</li><li>thinking and decision making</li></ul>
Theorist	<ul><li>structured situation, clear purpose</li><li>system or model observed</li><li>analysis and generalisation</li></ul>
Pragmatist	<ul><li>relevancy and usefulness</li><li>opportunity to tackle real problems</li></ul>

In almost all groups there is likely to be a mix of these types of learners with their preferred learning styles. So, while we cannot 'satisfy all of the people all of the time' we can perhaps 'satisfy all of the people some of the time' by ensuring that we try to provide elements of each learning style during the course. There may be occasions with certain types of group and/or course, and particularly with longer courses, when it is helpful to identify the preferred learning style of the group and to use this style more frequently. There are questionnaires available to identify learning preferences, e.g. Honey and Mumford (1986).

However, whilst most of us might have a preference for a particular learning style we can nevertheless learn comfortably and effectively with other styles. Furthermore, learning from experience can be seen as a four-stage cycle and that 'having the experience' or 'doing the activity' only is not enough. The other stages in the learning cycle are also important, i.e. reviewing the experience, concluding from the experience and planning the next steps, as shown below:

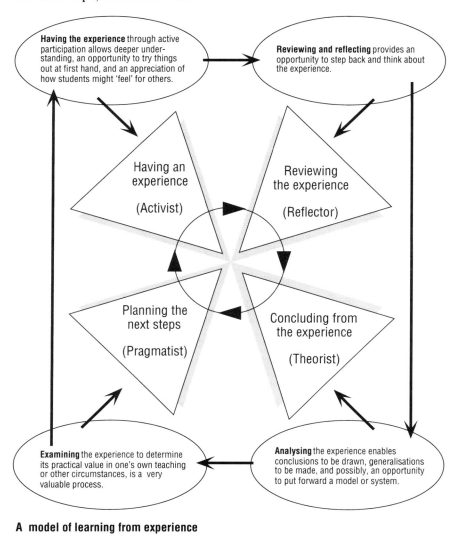

A model of learning from experience

ACTIVITY 16.1

In groups of two or three discuss and identify your preferred learning style(s) and whether you are primarily an activist, reflector, theorist or pragmatist, or some combination.

Levels of apprehension or anxiety

Tutors need to keep in mind the fact that many participants come along to a course with varying degrees of apprehension, even anxiety, particularly if active participation is required. This could be even more pronounced if, in addition, the subject matter deals with sensitive or controversial issues as, for example, in certain SATIS units.

ACTIVITY 16.2
In small groups brainstorm what you think some of the anxieties or apprehensions might be. Can you suggest any ways of minimising these? Compare your thoughts with those given on the following pages.

It is important, therefore, in planning and running such a session, that tutors try to minimise these concerns.

Will it be useful?

Will I enjoy it?

Will I know anyone?

Will it be interesting?

Do I know enough?

Is this course really for me?

Will it be boring?

Will I have to take part?

Will I be put on the spot?

Have I the confidence?

Will it be challenging and demanding?

These questions are particularly likely to cause anxiety if active participation and /or sensitive issues are involved.

Creating a climate for active participation
The tutor's role in creating such a climate is very important and can help to establish:

- a welcoming, non-threatening yet purposeful **atmosphere**;
- a more conducive **environment** for group interaction;
- an **empathy** between tutor and participants and between participants themselves;
- group **cohesion**.

Atmosphere

- Be relaxed, friendly, and easy going.
- Your manner can help to reduce apprehension.

Environment

- Ask for the seating to be arranged beforehand – in a circle or around a table, not in rows.
  - Arrive early in case you need to rearrange the room.
  - Ensure that the room is comfortable, with good ventilation.
  - Prepare photocopies/handouts/OHTs etc., in advance.

Empathy

- Don't feel that you have to be the 'expert'. Use phrases such as: 'share ideas', 'explore views' and 'I want to hear your feedback'.

- Don't be defensive of genuine criticism:
  - ideas/materials can be improved upon,
  - you are not 'flying a particular flag',
  - there may be hostility (recognise it and take it on board),
  - why not invite criticisms – they can be informative,
  - don't take criticism personally.
- Help participants feel that they have a valuable role to play.

Group cohesion

- Explain the structure of the session – if it is active, tell them (preferably) and tell them why.
- Intoductions 'warm-ups' are best done as an integral part of the session – they are less threatening if built naturally into a workshop.

163

A possible outline for a session

Here we provide a possible outline for a common type of INSET session, the purpose of which is to inform teachers about, for example, a new curriculum project and to examine/review/try out the student resource materials:

> Have a **clear purpose**. Use a range of learning stratagies (i.e. four stage cycle) and don't try to cover too much material.

> Give **general information** about the project and its underlying principles. Allow for a question and answer session.

> **Review** the student material. Where will it fit? How might it be used? Allow participants to enter into small group discussion.

> Allow participants to **try out** materials for themselves, in small groups. Follow-up with presentations to the whole group. Adapt student material if necessary, e.g. make more active, modify for less able, extension work, etc.

> **Review** the activities in small or whole group. The participants should leave with the confidence and the enthusiasm to try out the new student material

---

ACTIVITY 16.3

Imagine you have just taken over a fairly traditional department and the head has asked you to introduce more active learning approaches. Design an outline for a school-based INSET session (~1½ hours) which will:

- *heighten awareness of active learning in science;*
- *identify the need for change; and*
- *explore issues/problems which need to be addressed.*

Compare your ideas with the INSET activities on pages 165–70.

Leader's role

- Be enthusiastic, lively.
- Keep things moving along; have a good sense of pace.
- Stand back at first and move from group to group:
  - Join in.
  - Share ideas.
  - Invite comments.
- Involve the reticent.
- **Set firm deadlines.**
- Keep to times.
- Accept the right to sit it out.

- Don't be sidetracked.
- Avoid the **activity trap**:
  - Make time for review.
- Ensure there is adequate time available.
- Have an agenda:
  - 'How did you feel?'
  - 'What was its value?'
  - 'Were there any problems?'
  - 'What would you change?'
  - 'How would you use it?'
  - 'How would you do it?'

Basic pointers

- Plan in detail – especially timing!
- Know your material.

- Be enthusiastic – believe in it.
- Don't overload.

Exploring views on active learning and preparing for change

INSET Activity 1

Indentifying the personal and collective needs of a department in relation to active learning

Purposes:
- to establish the use of active teaching and learning by individual members of staff;
- to gauge the over-all impact within the science curriculum; and
- to identify priorities and develop an action plan for future development work.

Proposed structure of the session (approximate duration 1½–2 hours)

	Activity	Method	Resources required	Recommended time
1	Introduction and aims	Presentation to whole group	None	5 min
2	Participants complete proformas such as the one shown	Work individually	One proforma per participant	10 min
3	Participants share views with colleagues in order to establish similarities and diffferences in approach. Discuss strengths and weaknesses of these	Small groups of two or three	Paper or OHTs	10 min
4	Collate group responses to establish over-all departmental picture	Feedback from small group to whole group	OHT/flip charts	10 min
5	Compare agreed departmental requirements with existing individual methods and agree priorities for change	Whole group discussion	OHT/flip chart	15 min
6	Review existing curriculum materials and identify what support material is available to facilitate changes, and what needs to be developed	Small group activity followed by feedback and collation with whole group	Curriculum resource materials, OHTs or posters for feedback	40 min
7	Generate a departmental action plan for further activities and INSET. A model for such a plan is shown below	Small group or whole group discussion.	Paper	30 min

Proforma for INSET 1

Active teaching and learning strategy/approach	Which do I use now?	How frequently?	Which would I like to use?	Which will I focus on and what support do I need?
Role play				
Drama				
Small group discussion				
DARTS				
etc.				
etc.				

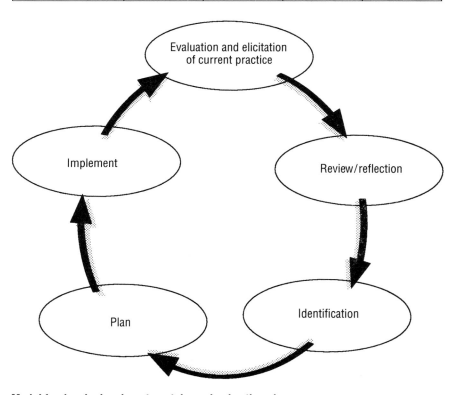

Model for developing departmental or school action plan

166

INSET Activity 2

What is active learning? What active learning strategies are available? What are the barriers to and pathways for implementation?

Purposes:

- to raise the issue of active learning with colleagues;
- to raise awareness of its benefits; and
- to begin to prepare the ground for change.

Proposed structure of the session (approximate duration 1½–2 hours plus optional workshop lasting 1–3 hours)

	Activity	Method	Resources required	Recommended time
1	Introduction: purpose	Presentation to whole group	None	5 min
2	Discuss what active learning is, i.e. what words or phrases describe a student working actively	Brainstorm in small groups. Feedback to whole group.	OHT 1	5–10 min
	Collate groups' results with tutor's	Whole group discussion	OHT 2	5 min
3	Discuss what active learning strategies can be used to support active learning.	Brainstorm in small groups. Feedback to whole group.	OHT 3	5–10 min
	Collate groups' results with tutor's	Whole group discussion.	OHT 4	5 min
4	Identify the characteristics of teacher-centred passive learning (TCPL) and student-centred active learning (SCAL).	Small group activity. Feedback to whole group.	OHT 5	10 min
	Collate (if desired) with tutor's result		OHT 6	
	It may be suggested that TCPL and SCAL are at two opposite ends of a continuum. That is not to say one should necessarily spend all the time at the SCAL end, but perhaps it would be better to make more frequent excursions into SCAL.			
5	Identify the barriers and then the pathways to SCAL.	Small group activity. Feedback to whole group.	OHT 7	10 min
	Collate with tutor's results.	Whole group discussion	OHT 8	10 min
6	*Optional*: Provide a range of ATLAS student activities to generate ideas and then ask participants to develop outlines of new activities themselves. Collect ideas into a pack and give a set to each participant.	Small group workshop	Selection of ATLAS student activities *or* other examples of 'active resources'	1–3 hours

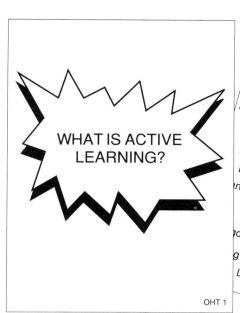

WHAT IS ACTIVE LEARNING?

OHT 1

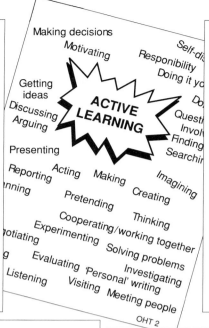

ACTIVE LEARNING

Making decisions
Motivating
Self-di...
Responibility
Doing it yo...
Getting ideas
Discussing
Arguing
Do...
Questi...
Invol...
Finding...
Searchin...
Presenting
Reporting Acting Making Imagining
...nning Creating
Pretending Thinking
Cooperating/working together
Experimenting Solving problems
...otiating
Evaluating 'Personal' writing Investigating
Listening Visiting Meeting people

OHT 2

IDENTIFYING ACTIVE LEARNING STRATEGIES

OHT 3

OHT 4

So what are the main differences between active and passive learning?

Teacher-centred passive learning is characterised by:

- teacher exposition,
- accent on competition,
- whole-class teaching,
- teacher responsible for the learning,
- teacher providing knowledge,
- students seen as empty vessels which need filling up,
- subject knowledge valued,
- teacher-imposed discipline,
- teacher and student roles stressed,
- teacher decides curriculum,
- passive student roles,
- limited range of learning styles and activities.

Student-centred active learning is characterised by:

- group work,
- accent on cooperation,
- resource-based learning,
- student takes responsibility for learning,
- teacher is a guide/facilitator,
- student ownership of ideas and work,
- process skills are valued,
- self-discipline,
- students seen as a source of knowledge and ideas,
- students involved in curriculum planning,
- students actively involved in learning,
- wide range of learning styles employed.

OHT 6

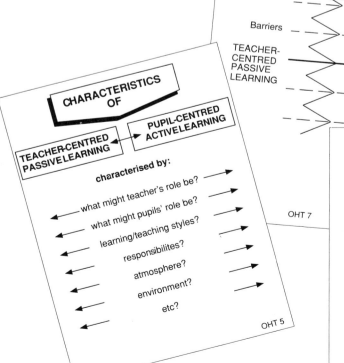

Barriers ---->
Pathways
TEACHER-CENTRED PASSIVE LEARNING
PUPIL-CENTRED ACTIVE LEARNING

CHARACTERISTICS OF
TEACHER-CENTRED PASSIVE LEARNING
PUPIL-CENTRED ACTIVE LEARNING

characterised by:

what might teacher's role be?
what might pupils' role be?
learning/teaching styles?
responsibilites?
atmosphere?
environment?
etc?

OHT 5

OHT 7

You can use the examples here to help you make your own OHTs.

- Change of role / loss of status → Allow students more responsibility for their own learning.

- May not be getting 'right' information → Don't be the 'font' of knowledge. Let students find out for themselves.

- Need to learn 'new' teaching strategies
- Pupils need to learn new learning strategies → Can be challenging and stimulating, enabling personal development for both teacher and student.

- Suspicion, cynicism among colleagues (and some students) → Communicate with colleagues. Tell them about the successes. A wide range of skills are developed

- Chaos, uproar, confusion, discipline problems → Introduce strategies at an early age. Establish 'ground rules' set by teacher and student together. Encourage student responsibility and self discipline. Value students' views.

- Time consuming → Accept that a range of important skills are being developed. Think small and short!

- Lack of student resources → More are required – this is happening.

OHT 8

INSET Activity 3

Reaching a concensus about active learning

Purpose:

- to establish a group/departmental concensus about the nature and value of active learning in science.

Structure of the session (approximate duration 2–3 hours)

Activity	Method	Resources	Time
1 Introduction: purpose and aims.	Whole group talk	None	5 min
2 Statement sorting: groups are presented with 20-plus cards giving favourable and unfavourable statements about teacher-centred/student-centred learning which appear on page 170. The task of the groups is to sort the cards into four of the categories on the choice chart. They should reach a concensus on each statement, avoiding the 'don't know' category.	Discussion in small groups of 2–3	Several sets of statement cards and a poster-sized choice chart. Strongly agree — Agree Don't know Strongly disagree — Disagree **Choice chart**	30–40 min
3 After dealing with as many of the statements as possible in the time available, statements are clipped together in each of the four categories for the plenary session.	Small groups	Paperclips	5 min
4 The spokesperson for each group first lists the statements which fell into the 'strongly agree' category. These are written on to a large sheet of paper or OHT for all to see. This is repeated for the statements in the 'agree' category. (If time is available, statements in the 'strongly disagree' category can be scrutinised.)	Whole group	Large sheets of paper and pens or OHTs/pens	2 min
5 Try to reach a concensus amongst the groups for as many statements as possible and a shared view about the issues surrounding active learning.	Whole group	None	15–20 min

The structure for this session is based on a session developed for a staff training day reported by Sean P. Moran in *SSR*, March, 1990, **71**, 256, although the content of the session is different.

List of suggested statements for INSET activity 3

- Active learning is time consuming.
- Active learning results in a loss of status for the teacher.
- Active learning is enjoyable and challenging for the students.
- Students are more motivated when they are actively involved in the learning process.
- Active learning is often chaotic and out of control.
- Active learning generates noise.
- Active learning encourages self responsibility and self discipline on the student's part.
- Student's should have a large part to play in organising their own learning.
- Teacher-centred learning means students get the facts of science right and this is the most important outcome.
- The teacher should decide what is to be learned.
- Students just waste time if given responsibility for their learning.
- The teacher is responsible for the learning.
- Teachers want to be teachers not facilitators.
- Students have an important role to play in recording their own progress and in the assessment process.
- Teacher-centred learning provides little opportunity for developing process skills.
- Students should be involved in curriculum planning and negotiation.
- Students with special educational needs can be catered for by using active learning strategies.
- Active learning reinforces teamwork and cooperation.
- Students should experience a variety of learning strategies.
- Teacher-centred learning reinforces competition.
- Students don't learn enough science through group discussion.
- It is very important that teachers allow time for creative and personalised writing in science.
- Students learn better when they are given the facts first.
- Students are likely to be confused if subjected to a wide range of learning styles.
- Most teachers would be happy to try active learning even if they knew that colleagues viewed it with suspicion and cynicism.
- The time needed for problem-solving activities is justified because of the wide-ranging benefits for pupils.
- There isn't much place for role play, drama or creative writing in science, these are best done in English.
- The National Curriculum allows no room for teachers to introduce innovative strategies into science lessons.
- It is much easier for students to avoid making a contribution in student-centred lessons than in teacher-centred lessons.
- Taking students on visits or bringing in visitors might be interesting but this doesn't teach much science.
- Science games are best used as end-of-term 'fillers' or for revision purposes only.

INSET
Course evaluation questionnaire

Course title: _____ Date: _____

1. What did you hope to get out of this course?

2. Did it fulfil your expectations?

3. Were the aims and purposes of the course made sufficiently clear and were they achieved?

4. Was the course interesting and enjoyable? For example:
   - Were the atmosphere and environment 'comfortable'?

   - Were you at all apprehensive and were you made to feel at ease?

   - Was there any attempt to generate a feeling of group cohesion/empathy?

   - Was there a good balance of inputs and activities?

   - Did you have a chance to review and reflect on your experiences?

   - Were you encouraged/able to contribute and comment?

5. Was the overall standard of presentation acceptable?

6. Has the course provided you with ideas and practical help that you can use and share with colleagues?

7. Are there any other comments or suggestions you would like to make?

Thank you for your help

Copymasters

Teacher's notes

The following notes are intended to offer guidance for the use of the student copymaster activities. The activities are grouped according to which active learning strategy they primarily represent.

Changes that affect animals and plants

This is essentially a discussion exercise intended to lead an understanding of hibernation, migration, the seasons, and day and night. It is also excellent material for exploring the technique called the 'jigsaw' method (see chapter 3). There are 5 sheets for this activity. The first four sheets can be used individually, employing the discussion agenda at the end of each. Alternatively, the same four sheets can be used in conjunction with the discussion agenda on the fifth sheet in a 'jigsaw' exercise:

1 Divide the class into groups of about four or five. (The size of groups will obviously depend on the size of class.) These are the home groups.
2 Each group is given a copy of the summary agenda.
3 Each home group is then split up, with one or two individuals going to each of four expert groups (again depending on class size). Each of these expert groups is given one of the four information sheets to look at, read and discuss. The presentation question for each agenda can be ignored or even whited out. The sheets increase in difficulty in the order: hibernation (easiest), migration, the seasons, day and night (hardest). These can be matched with student ability if desired.
4 Once discussion is complete, home groups can be reunited so that each member of a home group is now an 'expert' in a particular subject area. The questions on the summary agenda can then be looked at in the light of this new expertise.

You may wish to split classes into groups according to other determining factors. Agendas can be photocopied and handed out. We highly recommend that teachers explain to students exactly what they are being asked to do and why. The activity is particularly suited to low-level achievers.

Little Fuelham

This is a discussion exercise in which students are asked to decide on alternative sources of energy for an imaginary village. The agenda is intended to form a basis for this discussion. After the discussion is over, students are required to place appropriate installations onto the map provided. Students can then present their results and ideas to the rest of the class, either individually, in pairs or small groups.

Discussion techniques

This activity is a useful exercise in developing student awareness of discussion techniques. Students must cut out statements on good discussion practice and match them with humorous depictions of the same.

The rock cycle

Students should first of all read the information sheet concerning the rock cycle and the different types of rock. Sufficient time should be allowed for this, depending on ability, lesson time, etc. Students must then be split into groups and each group given a copy of the instruction sheet. Groups must compose a questionnaire of ten questions ready to be answered by another group. The group originating a questionnaire is responsible for marking it. The marking process itself is intended to be a source of discussion, and can assist in clarifying student understanding of the text. The activity ends with students using the knowledge gained to construct a labelled diagram of the rock cycle.

A nuclear reactor

This activity begins with students fitting together a jigsaw of a nuclear reactor. They must then read a passage on how nuclear reactors function. The questions listed below the text require students to highlight/underline pieces of text, and these are eventually used to label the completed jigsaw of the reactor. The completed exercise provides students with a labelled diagram of a nuclear reactor and related notes.

Coal

This activity looks at the formation of coal, coal types and coal mining. By reading text and answering questions on these subjects, students are required to fill in missing words, complete tables, and annotate diagrams. The exercise raises some environmental effects of coal mining.

The periscope

This activity can be treated simply as an active writing exercise, or also combined with investigation work on the periscope. Students who have previously made their own model of a periscope can use the copymaster as a focus for writing up an account of their investigation. By correcting a fictitious (and massively incorrect!) account, and having done the investigation themselves, students will be encouraged to write a good report. This exercise is particularly suited to students who do not warm to report composition once the 'fun' bit is over. The copymaster is a suitable homework exercise.

Who shall I sell to?

This activity is fundamentally an active writing exercise, but draws upon knowledge students acquire in a role play situation. The copymaster lists the views of a farmer and a developer who are both interested in purchasing an area of land from a third party. Students will need to be split into groups of 2–6 and asked to list the main points in each argument. Once they have done this, ask students to produce a questionnaire of around 10–12 questions, which can be used to find out what 'local opinion' is. It is important to emphasise balance and neutrality here (see page 153). The questionnaires can actually be tried out on the whole class. The class become the 'locals' and will hopefully reflect a broad range of opinion! Pairs of students, or individuals, can then use their results to write a report to Jean (the party selling the land) giving details of local opinion.

The alien who fell to Doncaster

Students must read a fictitious newspaper article about an alien, Akwa, landing on Earth. The article, together with the questions that follow it, encourage the reader to think about the water cycle, uses of water and its conservation. The copymaster aims to draw upon the imagination and creativity of students, who are asked to describe a meeting with Akwa in a second newspaper article. Try to get students to incorporate some of the knowledge they gain in their stories.

Presentation checklist

A pupil sheet to be used before any exercise involving presentation.
To begin with, get students to discuss the statements on planning a presentation given at the top of the copymaster. Students will eventually put the statements in the correct order and stick them onto the 'checklist' provided. Split the class up into groups. Size and membership (see page 27) will depend on the class. Give each student a copy of the statements and checklist, as they will be able to use the completed list for future presentation work. Don't forget to check them first.

The self-filling bucket

Students build and demonstrate a self-filling bucket from simple household items. It is important to reinforce the point that students will be asked to present their prototype for the self-filling bucket to the rest of the class at the end of the investigation. They can do this individually, in pairs or larger groups if necessary. Information is given on how a self-filling bucket works, but nevertheless try to check students' designs before too much water ends up on the laboratory floor! Supply a range of suitable materials. This is necessary to ensure that the class does not come up with 15 identical prototypes! Different solutions to the task will court healthy discussion during the presentations.

Apparatus
Materials to make bucket; yoghurt pots; plant pots; lemonade bottles; string; scissors; something safe to cut pots; water baths (sinks!); metre rules, tape measures; measuring cylinders/beakers; masking or insulating tape for making hinges.

Tomorrow it will be . . .

Students should study one of the weather maps given on the copymaster and write a short script for a TV weather forecast. They must then present their forecast to the rest of the class (NB The scripts students prepare should be videoed, if possible). Once again, students could do this in pairs or small groups, or even present to small groups rather than the whole class. Extension work might include playing an actual weather forecast on TV with the sound off, and asking students to compose the transcript.

Apparatus
OHTs of maps; overhead projector; alternatively have maps reproduced on chalkboard (more creative students could be asked to do this).

Boo's burger bar

Students should work in pairs. The role play exercise should begin with pairs filling in role sheets for the manager of the burger bar and the customer who is concerned about the amount of waste produced. This is to establish how each 'person' feels about the issue of waste packaging. The character development continues with the pairs thinking of questions and statements for the manager and customer. Armed with a role sheet and a list of questions students should then be able to act out an absorbing role play, covering, amongst others, the economic and environmental issues concerning paper and polystyrene packaging. As with any role play, it is important to emphasise to students that they act out the role they have been given and not their own personal views.

The greenhouse effect

During this role play activity students can begin to apply the ideas they have developed about combustion, in particular their knowledge of combustion products. The role play invites students to consider the global issues of the greenhouse effect.
Try to split students into groups of six, and make sure each group has a copy of the role sheet. Students should pick a role from a pile of roles folded up . Each student needs to be given time to study their role (and make notes) before they begin discussion. Aim to spend about 30 minutes on the actual discussion, and then move each group on to the production of an agreed press statement.

Kinetic theatre

This is an extremely active exercise in which students mime the behaviour of particles. There is an instruction sheet and an information sheet. Students should carefully read the latter first. This contains details on how solid, liquid and gaseous particles behave. The instruction sheet provides a variety of mimes for the students to enact. The mimes vary widely in difficulty and allow the teacher to allocate them according to student ability. For example, mimes a–c may be more suited to lower ability students, whereas d–g could be given to higher level achievers.

For each mime, students will need to be split into suitably sized groups, depending on ability and class size. Reinforce the point that one member of each group should narrate what is happening during a mime. Allow sufficient time for rehearsal of mimes and arrange the room accordingly. Students will need to be given space to move around in! Simple props may help some groups. Teacher's discretion may be necessary here.

Body data file

Variations in students' body measurements are recorded and then entered onto a computer data file. Copies of the body data card can be given to each student. The data file can then be used to answer questions, test hypotheses, and display data graphically. In doing this, students will need to order data, search for data and print out. Finally, students can present their findings to the class or in small groups. The charts they prepare will arm them with a valuable presentation tool!

The Planets

This activity is intended to be an IT exercise using a planet database on a computer. A suitable database can be found in the package 'Earth in space', available from RESOURCE (see page 82). A printed version of the information is given on the datasheet for this exercise, if the necessary computer resources are unavailable. Students must use the database to answer questions. The questions require students to data search, complete tables, plot graphs, and identify patterns in the planets. Students familiarise themselves with the scale of the solar system by making a mobile or pasting pictures onto paper. They will soon find this very difficult! Both these exercises necessitate the use of information from the database. This can either be done individually or in small groups. Groups are recommended if time on the computer is limited.

Sorting things

This activity requires students to classify objects by making observations about them and then use a branching database to sort the objects.

The teacher will need to display a variety of objects (eg stationery) on a bench. Split the class into small groups. Once students have chosen their objects, allow sufficient time for the recording of observations and collation of results (say 30 minutes). Make sure students have named each object, before they begin to sort them using the computer. A suitable branching database is 'BRANCH' (also available from RESOURCE).

The students will need to follow the instructions on the copymaster carefully for this part. Students must use yes–no questions to sort the objects. Some guidance may be needed initially. The observations students have made will help them with this.

Out on the trail

Students must plan a field trip to survey the various rock types used in local buildings. To do this they should use the planning agenda provided. The agenda encourages students to think about the purpose of the visit, its timing, the collection of information, sharing the workload, safety and social responsibility. The school coordinator should be consulted here. Students can write reports and present their findings as a follow-up exercise. The teacher may wish to initialise some library research into rock types before students embark on the field trip.

Noise patrol

Students are asked to play the part of an Environmental health officer in this activity, and respond to a complaint by a local resident. The activity prompts students into conducting a noise survey of their local High Street, or main thoroughfare. Students should plan for their visit first and clue card A will help with this. It is important to stress to students the safety aspects of this exercise, and group discussion of this before the survey will benefit both students and local residents! The school coordinator should be consulted here.

Apparatus
tape measures; decibel meters; tape recorders with external microphones; town plan; maps; clipboards

Local noise problems – arranging a visitor

Students consider noise pollution near an airport and then arrange for a visit to school by an environmental health officer. A clue card is included to aid planning (Note: Clue cards A and B are printed on one sheet and are intended for use with this activity and Noise patrol). This copymaster begins by asking students to answer questions concerning the noise problem caused by Britain's third largest airport, Manchester. The exercise acts as a springboard for inviting a local environmental officer into the school, to discuss noise problems in the area common to the school. Clue card B is intended to help students with the planning and usual areas of concern which need to be addressed when inviting a speaker into the school. The clue card can form the basis of a discussion.

Crops and climate

In this data handling activity, students are asked to plot graphs of rainfall and crop yield, and use these to form a hypothesis on the relation between the two. The graph can then be used to estimate missing values. Lower ability students may need some guidance on how to plot more than one graph on one set of axes.

Who's the fitter?

In this activity, the concepts of pulse rate and recovery period are used as an indication of fitness. Students are asked to plot the pulse rates of two girls and use the information to decide who is the fitter. The relationship between aerobic and anaerobic respiration is also investigated, together with lactic acid production leading to cramp. This second section is more suited to extension work. Students are required to plot the levels of oxygen, glucose, lactic acid, and fatty acids in a blood sample in order to answer questions relating to aerobic exercise and cramp.

Can I stop in time?

This data handling activity looks at the factors which affect the stopping distance of a motor car, in a breaking situation. Students should plot the stopping distances given, and use these to predict missing points. Students can then draw on this knowledge to answer questions about a real life scenario. The activity ends by looking at further factors that contribute to the overall stopping distance of a car. The copymaster is an ideal introduction to road safety, and the dangers associated with alcohol consumption when driving.

A new scoreboard?

A problem-solving exercise on pixel scoreboards forms the basis of this copymaster. The activity highlights the difference between analogue and digital signals. Students must design a scoreboard for a football club, to a budget of £10 000. Four pixel sizes are given to choose from, but students should consider quality of picture in addition to cost. Quality is observed in a very active way, by tracing of a simple picture using grids of varying coarseness (to simulate pixels). It would be very helpful for students if the grids on the second sheet of this copymaster were photocopied onto thinner paper in order to necessistate tracing. Alternatively, OHTs can be used to help with this process, if they are available. Paper can be held up to windows, although this may prove a little arm-aching when the finer grids are used. Students should summarise their findings in a report to the football club.

Blue Crystal Ltd

Students work as research scientists to dissolve copper sulphate crystals quicker. Each 'research team' begins with an imaginary budget of £100 000 and monies are either awarded for good practice or deducted for poor work. Put students into small groups of 3, 4, or 5, depending on class size. It is important to check groups' investigation plans, as copper sulphate is harmful. Make sure that students use frugal amounts of copper sulphate. Safety goggles must be worn. Each group should fill out an account sheet and present a final report on their findings to the director of Blue Crystal Ltd.

Apparatus
balance; watch glasses (for weighing); copper(II)

sulphate; pestles and mortars; spatulas; beakers; stirrers; measuring cylinders; thermometers; tripods; safety mats; bunsen burners; gauzes; safety goggles.

Hot cans

Students are invited to plan and perform an investigation to find the most suitable lime (from a sample of three) to use in self-heating cans. Put students into groups of 3, 4 or 5, depending on class size. Make up samples of lime as follows:

sample	amount of fresh lime (not anular)/g	amount of icing sugar/g
A	100	0
B	100	0.14
C	100	0.3

Although only very small quantities of icing sugar are used, it does slow down the reaction considerably. The reaction works best if the amount of lime is greater than the amount of water, e.g. a ratio of 2:1. Do not allow students to add small amounts of water to finely divided lime, as this can be explosive! Warn students of the heat the reaction can generate. Students should mix the lime and water quickly, and in a fume cupboard. Safety goggles must be worn.

Apparatus
balance; test tubes; spatulas; test tube racks; thermometers; watch glasses (for weighing); measuring cylinders; safety mats; safety goggles.

What a waste

The activity invites students to assume the role of an advertising agency, and produce a 3-minute radio advert for a waste recycling scheme. The activity combines discussion (agenda provided), script writing and recording onto magnetic media. Students need to split up into appropriately sized groups (say 3–6, depending on class size). If limited recording equipment is available, groups can write scripts first, and then record adverts one-by-one.

Apparatus
cassette recorder

Fossil evidence

An incomplete transcript of a radio interview on the subject of fossils must be completed by the reader. Split the class into appropriately sized groups and allow a short period for discussion. One students have had time to prepare answers for 'Doctor Brown', each group will then need to record the full interview. Recorded interviews should be swopped between groups, so that students can assess whether answers are correct or not.

Apparatus
cassette recorder

Powerful stuff

This activity is designed to be used with the CEGB video of the same name. The video can be obtained free from your local electricity board school liaison officer. Students should view the programme and then draw upon the knowledge to complete the crossword printed in the copymaster. Lower ability students could be permitted to use the rewind or freeze frame facilities to help them answer the questions. Rather than end the activity here, we suggest that students use the vocabulary to write a safety feature to a relative or friend. Posters, etc could also be prepared.

Electrolysis

This very active exercise requires students to simulate

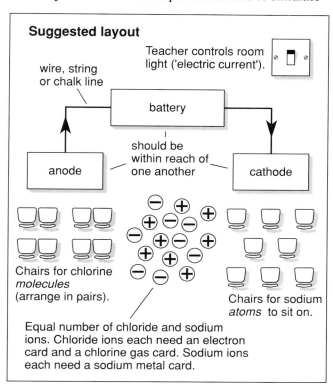

Suggested layout

Teacher controls room light ('electric current').

wire, string or chalk line

battery

should be within reach of one another

anode

cathode

Chairs for chlorine *molecules* (arrange in pairs).

Chairs for sodium *atoms* to sit on.

Equal number of chloride and sodium ions. Chloride ions each need an electron card and a chlorine gas card. Sodium ions each need a sodium metal card.

the electrolysis of molten sodium chloride. Each student adopts the role of either a chloride ion, a sodium ion, the cathode, the anode, or the battery. Role cards are provided, and it is suggested that the teacher photocopies and cuts out however many of each are required. The room being used should be checked to ensure that there is sufficient space for students to move around in safety. Once role sheets have been distributed, allow sufficient time for students to 'get into role'. Reinforce the point that they should do exactly what it says on their role sheets for the simulation to work.

Each student should have a badge for identification purposes in the simulation. Badges and cards can be made either by the students themselves, or by the teacher beforehand. The 'ions' will also require metal, gas, electron cards, depending on who they are. Finally, position the class for the start and switch on the light! The number of students simulating the battery, anode and cathode can be varied to ensure an even number of chloride and sodium ions. The electrolysis can be stopped using the room light in order to make teaching points, or give guidance.

States of matter

This activity reinforces the terms solid, liquid and gas by getting students to match examples. It is an easy-to-play, domino-like game in which students must match substances with states. Students can cut up their own set of dominoes and paste them onto card. A sheet of dominoes is ready for photocopying.

Enzyme action — lock and key model

In this activity, students make a model to simulate the catalytic mechanism of the enzyme maltase. Students need to copy the shapes in the copymaster onto coloured card, label them, and stick them onto a piece of paper, in the correct sequence, to model the action of maltase. The display can then be used by students to write a written description of the enzyme process.

Changes that affect animals and plants

For this topic, you will be divided up into groups, called **expert** groups. In your group, use the following **agenda** to help you discuss the information given below it.

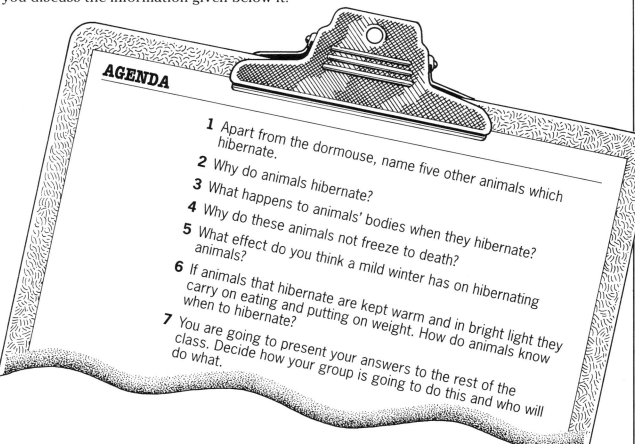

AGENDA

1 Apart from the dormouse, name five other animals which hibernate.

2 Why do animals hibernate?

3 What happens to animals' bodies when they hibernate?

4 Why do these animals not freeze to death?

5 What effect do you think a mild winter has on hibernating animals?

6 If animals that hibernate are kept warm and in bright light they carry on eating and putting on weight. How do animals know when to hibernate?

7 You are going to present your answers to the rest of the class. Decide how your group is going to do this and who will do what.

Hibernation

Hibernation, or 'winter sleep', is the way in which some animals escape the hardship of looking for food during the frost and snow of winter. They simply go to sleep until the warmer weather returns and their food supply is again plentiful.

Hibernation is not really that different from ordinary sleep, except that it is much deeper and lasts longer. Body temperature drops until it is almost as cold as it would be in death – about 1 °C. Because no energy is needed for movement, breathing becomes slower and the heartbeat grows faint and slow. Also, because so little energy is needed, the fat stored in the body is used up very slowly.

The dormouse

The dormouse is a hibernating mammal. During the autumn it eats so much food in a short time that it becomes very fat. When the temperature of the air drops to about 7 °C, the dormouse hibernates. It curls itself up into a tight ball, wraps its tail round its head and back, and puts its forepaws against its cheeks. The dormouse falls asleep in a nest of shredded honeysuckle bark. It lives off the fat stored in its body.

Other animals which hibernate

Another British mammal which hibernates is the hedgehog. The hedgehog rolls itself up and sleeps in a nest of dry leaves. Bats also hibernate. They do this in caves, old buildings and hollow trees. Some wake up and may be seen about on winter nights. Grey and red squirrels collect food for winter. They sleep more than usual, particularly during severe weather, but they do not hibernate in the way dormice and hedgehogs do. Badgers and some kinds of bear also sleep more during the winter.

Changes that affect animals and plants

For this topic, you will be divided up into groups, called **expert** groups. In your group, use the following **agenda** to help you discuss the information given below it.

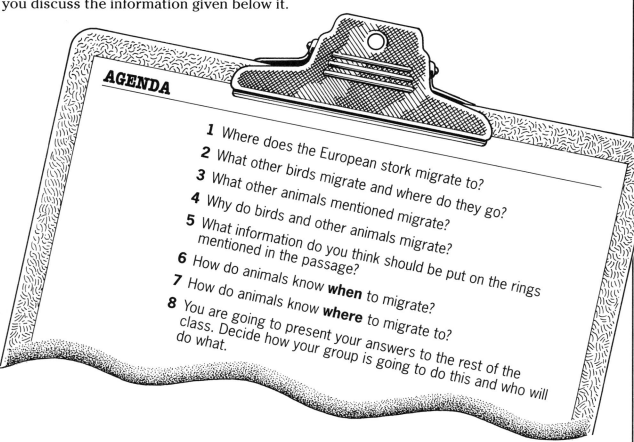

AGENDA

1 Where does the European stork migrate to?
2 What other birds migrate and where do they go?
3 What other animals mentioned migrate?
4 Why do birds and other animals migrate?
5 What information do you think should be put on the rings mentioned in the passage?
6 How do animals know **when** to migrate?
7 How do animals know **where** to migrate to?
8 You are going to present your answers to the rest of the class. Decide how your group is going to do this and who will do what.

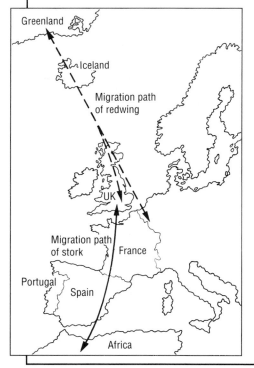

Greenland
Iceland
Migration path of redwing
UK
Migration path of stork
France
Portugal
Spain
Africa

Many animals make long journeys each year. Here are some examples:

The European stork
Storks fly from Northern Europe to Africa for the winter and return in the spring to breed. They often return to the same rooftops.

The redwing
The redwing migrates to the UK and Europe for the winter and flies back to Greenland for the summer.

Other animals
Caribou, or reindeer, travel long distances to feeding grounds in autumn and spring. Seals, especially the northern fur seal, spend much of their time at sea. They swim to places where they breed on almost the same day each year. The seals set out again for the open sea when the young have been weaned. In parts of Northern America some insect-eating bats migrate to warmer regions in the south, just as swallows do.

Ringing
Information about migration of birds can be obtained by putting a metal ring on their legs. In this way the birds can be identified when they settle in other places.

 Active Teaching and Learning Approaches in Science

Changes that affect animals and plants

For this topic, you will be divided up into groups, called **expert** groups. In your group, use the following **agenda** to help you discuss the information given below it.

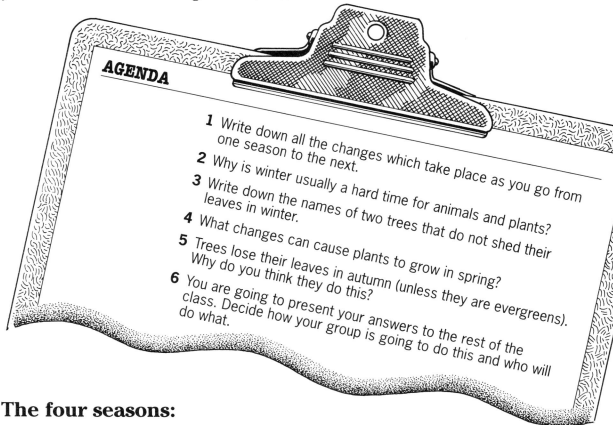

AGENDA

1 Write down all the changes which take place as you go from one season to the next.

2 Why is winter usually a hard time for animals and plants?

3 Write down the names of two trees that do not shed their leaves in winter.

4 What changes can cause plants to grow in spring?

5 Trees lose their leaves in autumn (unless they are evergreens). Why do you think they do this?

6 You are going to present your answers to the rest of the class. Decide how your group is going to do this and who will do what.

The four seasons:

Winter

Temperature around 0°C   Average rainfall 40 cm/day   Length of day 7 h

Spring

Temperature around 9°C   Average rainfall 25 cm/day   Length of day 9 h

Summer

Temperature around 20°C   Average rainfall 10 cm/day   Length of day 15 h

Autumn

Temperature around 12°C   Average rainfall 18 cm/day   Length of day 9 h

Active Teaching and Learning Approaches in Science

Changes that affect animals and plants

For this topic, you will be divided up into groups, called **expert** groups. In your group, use the following **agenda** to help you discuss the information given below it.

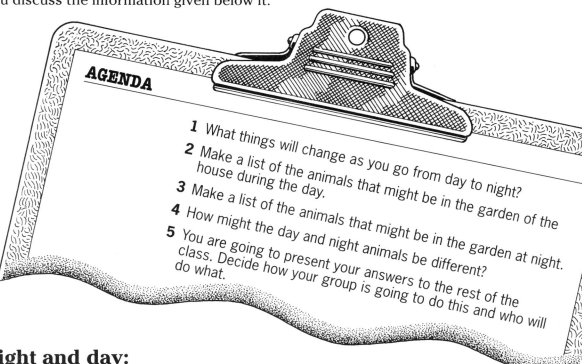

AGENDA

1 What things will change as you go from day to night?

2 Make a list of the animals that might be in the garden of the house during the day.

3 Make a list of the animals that might be in the garden at night.

4 How might the day and night animals be different?

5 You are going to present your answers to the rest of the class. Decide how your group is going to do this and who will do what.

Night and day:

   Active Teaching and Learning Approaches in Science

Changes that affect animals and plants

SUMMARY AGENDA

In your **expert** group you discussed one of the subjects: hibernation, migration, the seasons, night and day. You will now discuss all these subjects together with the other **expert** groups. You will do this in a **home** group, using the agenda below.

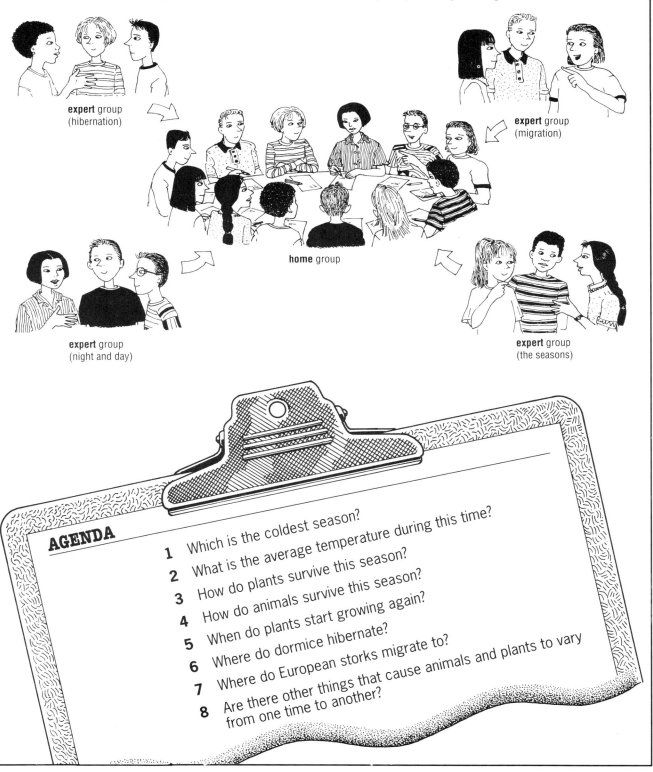

expert group (hibernation)

expert group (migration)

home group

expert group (night and day)

expert group (the seasons)

AGENDA

1 Which is the coldest season?
2 What is the average temperature during this time?
3 How do plants survive this season?
4 How do animals survive this season?
5 When do plants start growing again?
6 Where do dormice hibernate?
7 Where do European storks migrate to?
8 Are there other things that cause animals and plants to vary from one time to another?

Little Fuelham

You will use the following agenda to have a discussion about the information on this sheet. You will then prepare a presentation for the rest of the class.

AGENDA

1 What are the disadvantages of using fossil fuels (e.g. coal, oil and gas)?

2 What other sources of energy can you think of?

3 How can these energy sources be used?

4 What conditions are needed to use the energy effectively?

5 What are the advantages and disadvantages of these sources of energy?

6 Look carefully at the map and decide which sources of energy you will use. Where will you build any equipment or buildings which will be needed?

The map shows an area in Wales. A new village called *Little Fuelham* is going to be built. The village will be **'environmentally friendly'**. It will **not** consume any non-renewable fuels, e.g. coal, oil or gas.

When you have completed your discussion:

- mark the position of each energy source on the map,
- copy out and complete the table to summarise your discussion,
- prepare a short presentation for the rest of the class.

Source	Advantages	Disadvantages	Reasons for choosing position

© Sheffield City Polytechnic/CollinsEducational 1992   *Active Teaching and Learning Approaches in Science*

Discussion techniques

This exercise shows some important points to remember when taking part in a discussion. Cut up the page along the dashed lines. Match each cartoon with its correct comment, and glue them all to a plain piece of paper.

Get one member of the group to write down the most important points discussed and any decisions that are made.	Always let other people finish speaking, even if you wish to say something.	Even if you feel shy you must take part in the discussion.
Remember that discussion helps you learn and other people learn.	Be ready to change your mind if you are wrong.	Use a paper and pencil during discussions.
Remind the group if someone has said something important.	Listen carefully to what everyone says.	Do not show off.
If you do not understand anything ask for it to be explained.	If you do not agree with someone do not shout at them.	Explain things if two people do not understand each other.

The rock cycle

Read the following information on the three types of rock: **igneous**, **sedimentary** and **metamorphic**. You must read this information carefully to carry out the instructions that follow it.

IGNEOUS
(from the Latin word *ignis*, meaning **fire**)

Igneous rocks are formed when liquid rock, called **magma**, solidifies. If magma solidifies under the earth's surface it only becomes visible when the rock above it is eroded away. Granite in the Lake District is an example of this. However, sometimes molten rock bursts through the Earth's surface to form a volcano. This molten rock is called **lava** which can solidify to form basalt. In both cases, the rock solidifies to form crystals. When it is exposed at the Earth's surface, igneous rock can be weathered or eroded away by ice, wind and water. The rock breaks into smaller pieces. Examples of igneous rock include **granite** and **basalt**.

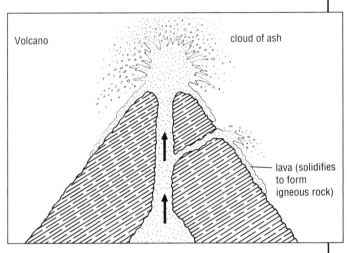

SEDIMENTARY
(from the word **sediments**)

Sedimentary rocks are broken pieces of rock and may include fragments of animals which have been carried and then deposited by wind, water or ice. The broken-up bits of rock are mainly sand, silt and clay. As the sediments build up on top of each other they form layers. Eventually the layers, under pressure from the weight of those layers above, are turned into sedimentary rock. This process is called **lithification**. Examples of sedimentary rock are **sandstone** and **limestone**.

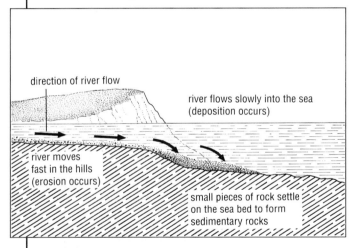

METAMORPHIC
(means to **change in form**)

Igneous and sedimentary rocks in the Earth's crust can be exposed to high temperatures and pressures, e.g. if they are near a volcano. This causes the rocks to change. They become what are known as metamorphic rocks. If the temperature and pressure are high enough, the rocks melt to form a magma. The magma can crystallise to form igneous rock.

Examples of metamorphic rock include **marble** (formed from limestone) and **gneiss** (formed from granite).

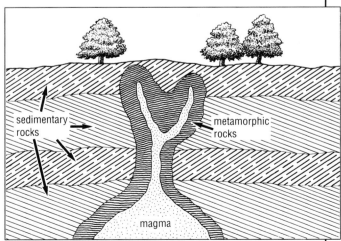

If **any** of these rock types are exposed at the Earth's surface, they are weathered and eroded to form new **sediments**.

The rock cycle

1 In your group, make up ten questions on what you have read.

2 Swop your questions with another group.

3 Answer the questions you are given. If you have read the information carefully, you should be able to do this without reading it again. Answer as many questions as you can without looking at the information.

4 Give your answers to the other group, and collect their answers.

5 Mark the answers to your questions. Now discuss the questions you wrote, their answers and how you marked them, with the other group.

6 You will realise from reading the information carefully that one type of rock can be changed into another. In turn, this can be changed into the original form again. The rock types can be arranged in a **cycle**. Cut out the pieces below and arrange them in a 'rock cycle'. When you are happy that it is correct, ask your teacher to check it. If it is correct, glue it into your book or file.

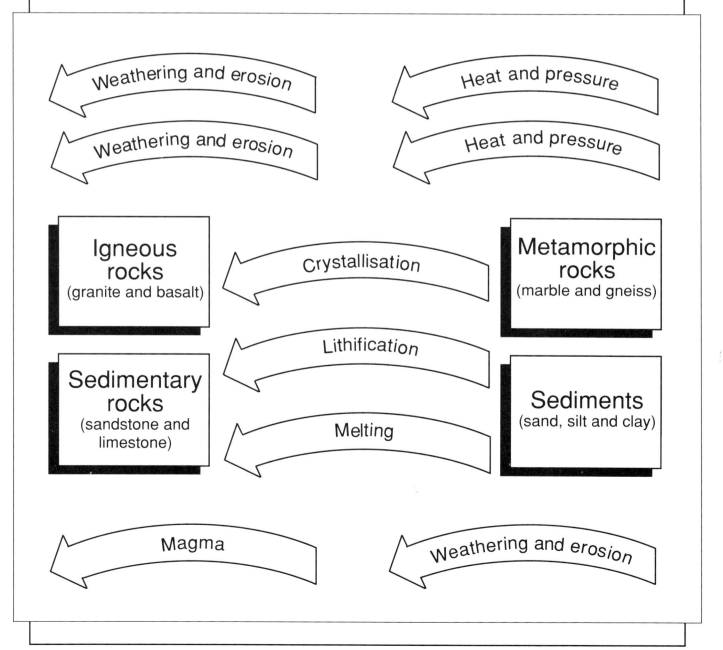

A NUCLEAR REACTOR

Cut out the pieces of the jigsaw and fit them together. Stick them down on to a piece of paper when they are in the correct order.

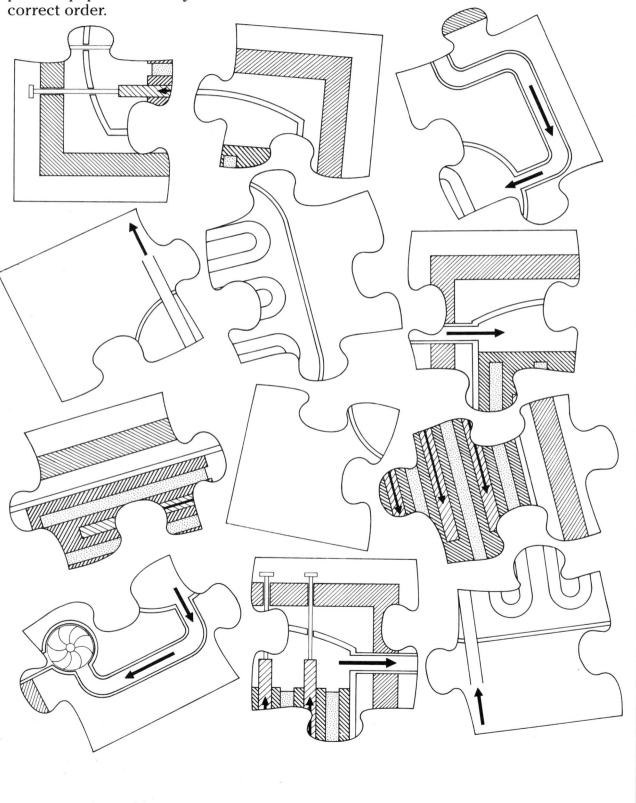

     Active Teaching and Learning Approaches in Science

A NUCLEAR REACTOR

Read this passage and then follow the instructions after it:

In this type of nuclear reactor (see jigsaw) a chain reaction takes place in the uranium fuel rods. The chain reaction is caused by the release of neutrons from uranium 235 in a process called fission. When fission happens an atom splits into smaller pieces and releases certain particles. In this case the important particles are called neutrons. The neutrons hit other uranium atoms which split up and release still more neutrons. These neutrons in turn split up more atoms and the process continues.

The uranium fuel rods of the reactor are set inside a graphite core. The core absorbs some of the neutrons and slows the chain reaction down. Uranium 235 releases energy more efficiently when fission is slow. The graphite core is called a moderator. The chain reaction can also be controlled using boron control rods. These absorb neutrons better than the uranium. The boron rods can be lowered into the reactor core, and raised again. If the rods are fully lowered into the core, the reacton will stop. As the rods are pulled out less and less neutrons are absorbed and the chain reaction speeds up again.

Every time an atom splits, energy is released. This energy heats up carbon dioxide gas which is pumped through the core. The hot gas passes through a heat exchanger which turns water into steam. The hot steam is then used to drive turbines which generate electricity. The entire reactor core is surrounded by a thick concrete shield to prevent dangerous radiation escaping.

1 Use coloured pencils for the following:

a Ring in black the name of the fuel used in the nuclear reactor. Underline in black the word which describes what type of reaction occurs. What is the name of the important particle released by this reaction? Underline the name of this particle in red.

b Underline in blue the word which describes the splitting of a nucleus and the sentence which describes what happens when this splitting occurs.

c Ring in orange the name of the part that the fuel rods are set in. Underline in orange the job this material does. Ring in orange another name for this part of the reactor.

d Ring in green the name of the things that can be raised or lowered. Underline in green the reason why these things are raised and lowered.

e Ring in yellow the name of the gas which is heated up by the reactor. What does the hot gas pass through as it is pumped out of the reactor? Ring this in red.

f What does the heat from the hot gas turn water into? Ring this in blue.

g Underline in blue the sentence which describes how electricity is generated.

h Ring in green the part of the reactor which is used for protection. Underline in green the sentence which explains how this structure works.

2 Use all the words you have *ringed* to label the diagram you made using the nuclear reactor jigsaw.

Active Teaching and Learning Approaches in Science

COAL

THE FORMATION OF COAL

1 Copy out the passage and fill in the missing words using the list below it.

Coal forms over a period of millions of years. Long ago, forests of _____ and other woody plants _____ and were covered with layers of soil and _____. Over a period of many years the _____ of the rocks above turned the _____ into coal.

rock   trees   pressure   died   wood

TYPES OF COAL

2 Copy out the table below and complete it by reading the passage here. You might need to estimate some of the details.

Coal consists mainly of the elements carbon and hydrogen. Different types of coal have different amounts of these elements, depending on how deep the plant material was buried. The deeper the material was buried the greater the pressure it was under. A small amount of pressure causes **peat** to form. This soft, brown material is therefore found near the surface. At slightly greater depths the peat is turned into a soft brown coal called **lignite**. Lignite contains about 70 per cent carbon. At even greater depths, **bituminous coal** is formed. The deepest coal is called **anthracite**. This is black and very hard. It contains over 90 per cent carbon and gives a great deal of heat when it is burned.

Type of coal	Colour	Hardness	Carbon content (%)	Hydrogen content (%)

3 Are there any patterns between the type of coal and their features?

4 Which type of coal will make the best fuel? Explain your choice.

          Active Teaching and Learning Approaches in Science

COAL MINING

5 Read the following passage carefully:

In recent years, more and more people have been using oil and gas as fuels. However, coal still provides the UK with up to 40 per cent of its energy. Coal will still be around when oil has run out. If consumption stays at its present rate there will be enough coal to last the UK another 800 years.

Coal is normally found in layers called **seams**. If the seam is below the surface it is called a **concealed** seam. If it comes to the surface it is called an **exposed** seam. Exposed seams can be mined by digging out the coal at the surface and carrying it away. This is called **open-cast** mining. Once the surface coal has been mined a channel is dug underground along the seam. This is called **drift** mining. However, there is a limit to how far this channel can be dug. Eventually the coal must be reached from directly above by digging a shaft from the surface. This is called **shaft** mining.

6 Stick the diagram below in your notes:

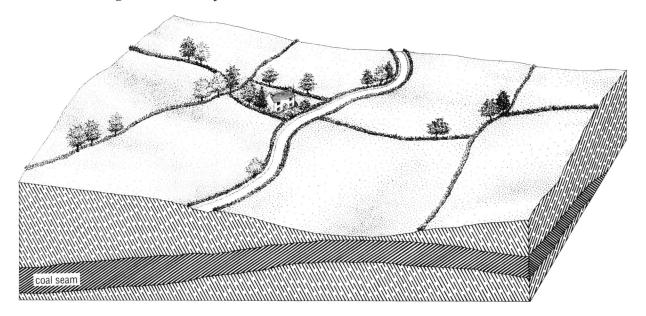

coal seam

7 Use the previous passage to help you show:
   a an area suitable for an open-cast mine,
   b the starting position for a drift mine,
   c a shaft mine.

8 For each of the three types of mine, explain why you have chosen your position. (You can do this by explaining the basic differences between the three types of mine.)

9 Answer the following:
   a Give one reason why there has been an increase in the use of oil and gas recently.
   b How much longer will the UK's supply of coal last?
   c What is the correct name for a layer of coal?
   d Which of the three types of coal mine damages the appearance of the environment most?
   e Are there any other environmental problems as a result of coal mining?

THE PERISCOPE

The report below is of how a student made a periscope at school. The student made **ten** mistakes. Rewrite the report so that it is correct.

To help you do this, think about the following:

- Is the diagram drawn correctly?
- Is the diagram labelled correctly?
- Is any of the apparatus incorrect?
- Is any of the apparatus missing?
- Are there any mistakes in grammar or spelling?
- Is the science correct?
- Is anything missing from the report? If so, should you add this?

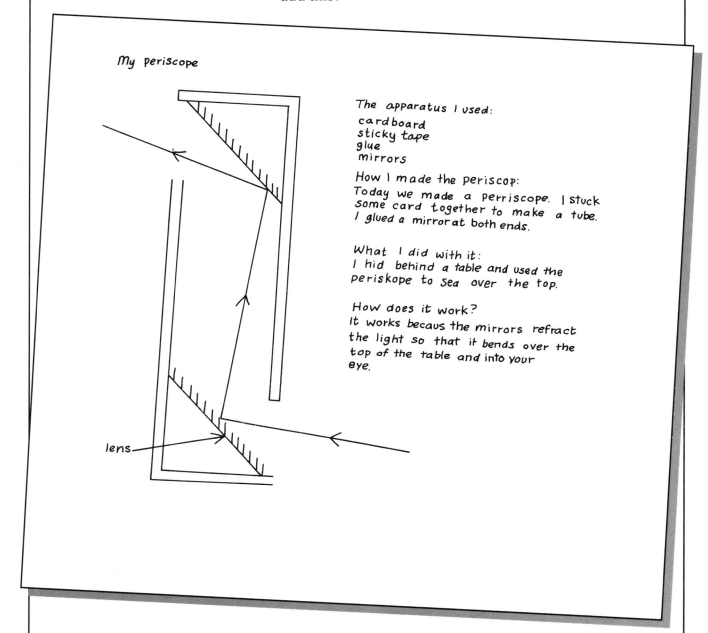

My periscope

lens

The apparatus I used:
cardboard
sticky tape
glue
mirrors

How I made the periscop:
Today we made a perriscope. I stuck some card together to make a tube. I glued a mirror at both ends.

What I did with it:
I hid behind a table and used the periskope to sea over the top.

How does it work?
It works becaus the mirrors refract the light so that it bends over the top of the table and into your eye.

      Active Teaching and Learning Approaches in Science

Who shall I sell to?

Jean Greenfield has some land she wishes to sell. Two people wish to buy it: a local developer who wants to build a golf course and a neighbouring farmer who wants to buy more land for organic farming.

In pairs, read the cases made by the local developer and the farmer:

> There is growing demand for organically grown vegetables. More farmland would help to meet the demand for organic vegetables and keep the price down. I do not intend to use any chemical fertilisers on the land so I will not be causing any pollution. Also, I do not intend to destroy coppice wood or hedgerows, so the present land will retain its charm.

> There is a lot of interest in golf in this area, but there are very few facilities. A new golf course would be very popular. New jobs will be created for local people, either working in the clubhouse or as greenkeeping staff. The golf course would attract people from surrounding areas, so local shops and businesses would also benefit. People may even wish to move here. I also believe that the proposed golf course will be more attractive to look at than the present land.

> What shall I do?

farmer   developer   Jean

What you need to do:

1 On a piece of scrap paper, write down the main points each person uses to persuade Jean to sell her land to them.

2 You work for a market research company. Jean asks you to find out the opinions of people in her area. Design a questionnaire of 10–12 questions, which could be used to help Jean make up her mind. Make sure the questionnaire is fair and doesn't favour either the local developer or the farmer.

3 Pretend that your class are the people who live in Jean's area. Ask all the people in your class to answer the questionnaire.

4 Use your results to write a report to Jean which gives the feelings of the local people.

The alien who fell to Doncaster

ALIEN LANDS IN SOUTH YORKSHIRE

V. Nus, Space correspondent

In an exclusive interview for the Daily Waffle, Joe Ford describes how he met an alien from the planet Dryasadustia and showed it around Doncaster.

"I found the alien in my back garden," reveals Joe. "It just landed there, right in the middle of my pond. I asked the alien where it came from. It told me its name was Akwa, from the planet Dryasadustia. Akwa was amazed by my pond. Apparently the beings on Dryasadustia are only allowed one litre of water a day, because it's so hot and dry there. Akwa told me that it had been exploring all the local planets to see if it could find some water to take home."

"I decided to take Akwa round Doncaster and show all our water. We had lunch at a burger restaurant. Akwa got really excited when it saw the ice in our drinks. Akwa had never seen ice before. After I had explained what ice was, Akwa thought that it might solve the problem on Dryasadustia. Perhaps Akwa could transport big chunks of ice to bring back home. I had a brilliant idea. We flew off to the Arctic Circle and Akwa chose a huge iceberg. We loaded the iceberg into the spaceship and then Akwa flew me back to Doncaster. Akwa waved goodbye there (with all four hands!) and left for home. It was so amazing, and I bet no one will believe me."

What you need to do:

Using your scientific knowledge and your imagination, discuss the following questions:

1 How do you think the people of Dryasadustia save water?
2 How do the plants and animals on Dryasadustia survive?
3 What would you do if you could only have one litre of water a day?
4 What would you do if you met someone from another planet?
5 What would you say to the alien?

6 What would the alien think about the way water is used in your area?
7 Would the alien be happy about the way in which you use water?
8 Would the alien think we waste water?
9 How would you explain to the alien what ice is?
10 How would you explain how people such as eskimos survive cold climates?
11 If you were given £1 million, how would you use it to help people who have very little water?

Write your own newspaper article describing a meeting with Akwa. Use your answers to help you.

    Active Teaching and Learning Approaches in Science

Presentation checklist

Discuss the statements in the boxes and decide on which order they should go in. When you have done this, cut them out and stick them in the correct boxes in the checklist.

What will be the basic outline or structure of your presentation?	Who in the group will do which part of the presentation?
What information does your audience already know?	Group rehearsal of all the separate parts.
What questions might you be asked and what are the answers?	Rehearse your part and time it.
Write your script and memory cards to help you if you forget what to do or say.	Prepare your visual aids.

Every time you are asked to make a presentation, use this checklist to make sure that your group has covered everything.

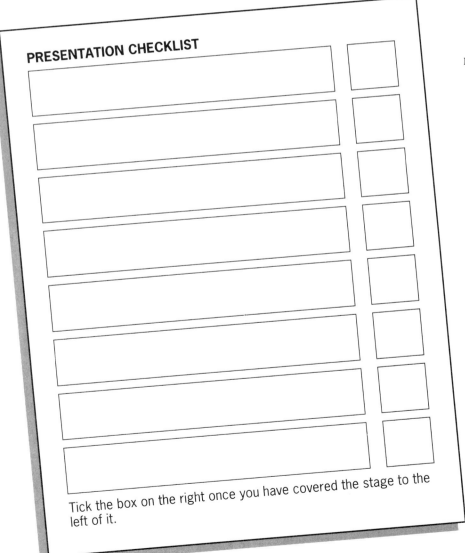

PRESENTATION CHECKLIST

Tick the box on the right once you have covered the stage to the left of it.

Active Teaching and Learning Approaches in Science

The self-filling bucket

You are going to design and then build a self-filling bucket. Once you have made the bucket you will be asked to present it to the rest of your class and explain how it works.

While you are making the bucket think about the following:

– How will I explain how the bucket works?
– Do I need any diagrams to help me explain?
– Will the diagrams be shown on a blackboard, an overhead projector, or some other way?
– Will I need someone else to help me with the presentation?

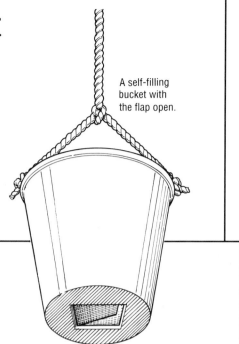

A self-filling bucket with the flap open.

The self-filling bucket is for lifting water out of a well. It looks like an ordinary bucket except that it has a flap (like a trap door) in the bottom. If you lower an ordinary bucket into a well it often floats and does not fill up with water. The flap in the self-filling bucket lets water in, but closes as the bucket is lifted.

How does it work?

The bucket flap is hinged along one side. It lifts up if it is pushed from below. It cannot go further down than the bottom of the bucket.

When the bucket is lowered into the water, the water underneath the bucket lifts the flap.

When the bucket is pulled out of the well, the water in the bucket pushes the flap down. The bucket can then be pulled to the top of the well.

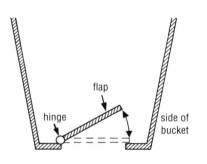

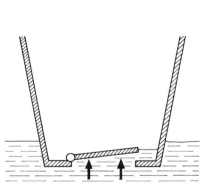

water pushes flap upwards

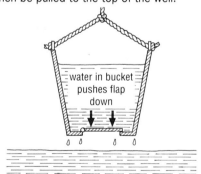

What you need to do:

1 Build your own self-filling bucket. (You can use a yoghurt pot, plant pot or lemonade bottle.)

2 Get it checked by your teacher.

3 Fill your bucket with water by lowering it into a water bath. The rim of your bucket must not go beneath the level of the water, and you are allowed only 20 seconds to fill it.

4 Carry the bucket of water for a distance of 10 metres and then empty the contents into a beaker. Record how much water you manage to carry using your bucket.

Things to think about:

How big will your bucket be? If the bucket is too big it may not be strong enough. If the bucket is too small it will not hold very much water, and it will be difficult to make.

How can you make a hinge? Sticky tape can be used as a hinge. Some materials bend easily and will not need a hinge. Whatever you use, the hinge must not leak too much and it should only bend upwards.

     Active Teaching and Learning Approaches in Science

Tomorrow it will be...

All the BBC weather presenters have colds! You will have to take their place and present the weather forecast. Choose one of the weather maps and write a short script for the weather forecast. Your script should last about 1 minute. When you have prepared the script you will be asked to present it to the rest of your class.

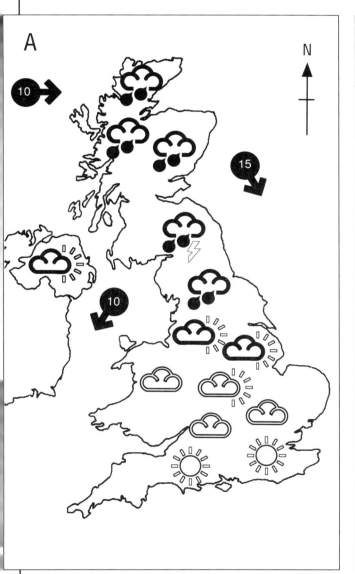

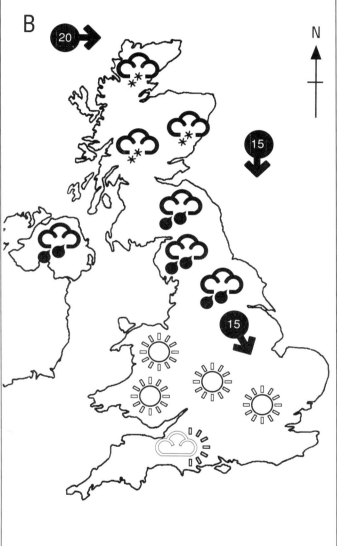

While you are waiting to present your forecast, design and fill in a table which includes all the BBC weather symbols and what they stand for. Make up some of your own symbols if you have time.

Find out if the ITV weather symbols differ from those used by the BBC.

BOO'S BURGER BAR

You are going to take part in a short role-play between the manager of a burger bar and a customer. Before you do this you will need to prepare role sheets for the two parts. This will help you and your class to act out the role-play. Work in pairs.

A new burger bar has opened locally and all the food is to be put into polystyrene containers and paper bags, whether the customer eats in or out. A customer asks to see the manager to complain about the waste, and suggest some alternative ways of serving the food. The manager wants to serve the food quickly and with the least fuss. The burger company is not worried about the cost of packaging and waste.

What you need to do:

1 Fill in the two role sheets. Give each character a name. Describe how you think each person will feel, what their views will be and what each will want to happen.

Role Sheet: customer	**Role Sheet: manager**
Name:	Name:

2 Think of questions the customer might ask the manager and statements that the customer might make. Write these in the customer box. Do the same thing for the manager's questions and statements to the customer.

Questions and Statements:	**Questions and Statements:**
Customer	Manager

3 Cut out the role sheets and question–statement boxes. Use these to help you and your partner to perform a short role-play between the customer and the burger bar manager.

© Sheffield City Polytechnic/CollinsEducational 1992 *Active Teaching and Learning Approaches in Science*

The greenhouse effect

You are going to take part in a role-play between different members of a United Nations committee. You will be discussing the greenhouse effect.

NEWS   23 June

United Nations committee meeting to discuss the greenhouse effect

A United Nations committee wants to make some comments about the likely effect of the so-called greenhouse effect. There are six people on this committee and each person has specialist knowledge on the greenhouse effect, together with strong ideas and opinions.

What you need to do:

1 Get into groups of six. Your teacher may have already put you into groups.

2 Elect a chairperson for the group.

3 Collect a role sheet and cut it up along the dashed lines. Fold the pieces of paper up so they cannot be read, and put them in a pile at the centre of the table. Each person should now pick up one of the pieces of paper, which will describe the role they are going to play.

4 Your role-play name is at the top of the piece of paper – one name for a male and another for female. Read your role carefully, and then make a list of the main views and concerns of your character. Now try to remember these without referring to your list.

5 Start the discussion with everybody introducing themselves to the group (name, who they work for, etc.) and giving their thoughts on the greenhouse effect. Listen carefully to everybody's comments.

6 Each person can then say who they agree with and who they disagree with, and why.

7 Your teacher will tell you how long your discussion should last. At the end, your group will have to write a statement to the press saying what you have agreed upon and what things you disagreed about.

United Nations Committee role sheet

Mr G. Redhead/Ms D. Weiguo
Earth science expert

You are concerned about the amount of carbon dioxide entering the atmosphere. You believe that as more fossil fuels are burned, carbon dioxide levels increase. This creates the greenhouse effect on Earth, because heat energy is trapped by the carbon dioxide layer. You think less fossil fuels should be burned.

Mr S. Good/Ms P. Idris
Expert chemist

You are not very concerned about the build-up of carbon dioxide in the atmosphere. Research has shown that large amounts of the gas dissolve in sea water. You think that the sea prevents carbon dioxide building up. However, you know that carbon monoxide and some nitrogen oxides (both made by petrol engines) can also cause the greenhouse effect. These gases are not removed by the sea so easily. You think catalytic converters should be fitted to all car exhausts to reduce these gases. (The converters increase the cost of one car by up to £500.)

Ms W. Fleming/Mr H. Bolder
Spokesperson for the Worldwide Association of Car Manufacturers

Your main concern is to protect your industry. Whilst you are constantly improving fuel consumption, and reducing the pollutants put out by cars, you will not agree to any reduction in car making. The companies you represent make and sell cars for a profit and nothing should interfere with that process.

Ms T. Dujon/Mr K. Watkins
Chief geologist to a firm of international oil consultants (A geologist is a person who studies the Earth's crust)

Your main concern is that there is only a fixed amount of fossil fuel remaining inside the Earth. You believe that these resources should be conserved, and not wasted by being burned.

Ms S. Rahman/Mr Z. Kumar
Environmental spokesperson for the United Nations

Your main concern is that as more and more oxygen is being converted to carbon dioxide by burning fossil fuels, the Earth cannot replace the oxygen. The oxygen is needed by many lifeforms to survive. You are especially worried about the destruction of the rainforests, which are needed to convert large amounts of carbon dioxide back into oxygen by photosynthesis.

Mr L. de Costa/Ms A. Vieira
Economic spokesperson for Brazil

You are very concerned about the following:
– attracting business to your country,
– using your country's vast natural resources,
– opening up large areas of the rainforests for the production of timber, building much needed roads, mines, and farms.

All this will enable poor and unemployed people to make a living from the land and its resources.

 Active Teaching and Learning Approaches in Science

Kinetic theatre

States of matter

In your group, read the information sheet on particles. You should try to understand all the information before you do a mime.

Choose one of the following topics:

a the particles in a solid;
b the particles in a liquid;
c the particles in a gas;
d the particles in a melting solid;
e the particles in a freezing liquid;
f the particles in a boiling liquid;
g the particles in a condensing gas.

Discuss the topic you have chosen in your group. Try to decide how the particles would behave. Rehearse a mime to show this, and then present it to the rest of the class. Remember that one person in your group should explain what the people in the mime are doing.

Expansion and contraction

The facts:

• If a substance is heated the particles move faster.
• If a substance is cooled down the particles move slower.
• The volume of most substances increases when they are heated.
• The volume of most substances decreases when they are cooled down.

Study the information sheet again, and look at the facts you are given here. Discuss what happens to substances when they are heated and cooled. How can you mime these? Rehearse a mime and then present it to the rest of the class. **Remember!** It is the substance that changes volume **not** the particles.

Heat transfer (conduction and convection)

The facts:

• If you heat one end of a metal bar the other end soon gets hot. This is called **conduction**.
• If a liquid is heated, the hot particles vibrate faster and so move apart. This makes the hot part less dense than the surrounding liquid so it moves up to the surface of the liquid. Away from the heat, the same particles cool down and move slower. This is called **convection.**
• Hot air is less dense than cold air. Hot air rises and cold air falls. This also is called **convection**.

Discuss, and then mime, how the particles in the metal conduct heat from one end of the bar to the other.

Discuss and mime how the particles in a liquid or a gas move during convection.

Kinetic theatre

Once you have read this information sheet you will perform a short piece of mime (in groups) to model the behaviour of particles in different states. While you perform the mime, one person in your group needs to explain to the rest of the class what you are doing, and why. If you wish, you can use simple props.

All substances are made up of atoms and molecules. Molecules are made up of atoms joined together. The state a substance is in depends on how its particles are arranged. There are three states – solid, liquid and gas. In all these states the particles are constantly moving around.

Solids: e.g. ice at –20 °C

1 Have a definite size and volume.
2 Have a definite shape.
3 Have a definite mass and weight.
4 Have several outside surfaces.
5 If solids are heated enough, they melt.

The particle picture:

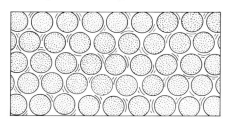

a Particles are close together.
b Particles usually in a regular pattern.
c Particles vibrate.
d Particles held together.
e The particles vibrate faster when they are heated.

Liquids: e.g. water at 20 °C

1 Have a definite size and volume.
2 Have no shape of their own. Liquids take the shape of the container they are in.
3 Have a definite mass and weight.

The particle picture:

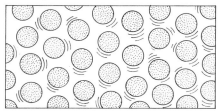

a Particles close together.
b Particles arranged in no particular pattern. The pattern always changes.
c Particles move randomly.
d Particles held together.
e The particles move faster, when they are heated.

Gases: e.g. steam at 120 °C

steam

1 Have a definite size and volume.
2 Have no shape of their own. Completely fill the container they are in.
3 Have a definite mass and weight.
4 Have no surface of their own.

The particle picture:

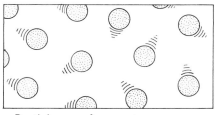

a Particles are far apart.
b Particles are not arranged in a pattern. The pattern always changes.
c Particles move quickly and randomly.
d Particles are not held together – they are free to move around.

    Active Teaching and Learning Approaches in Science

Body data file

Collect the following information about yourself and use it to complete the form.

Body data card

1 **NAME**				2 Class		3 Sex M/F
4 Hair colour (tick one)	black	dark brown	light brown	blond	red	other
5 Eye colour (tick one)	brown	green	blue	grey		other
6 Height (m)						
7 Mass (kg)						
8 Arm length (cm)						
9 Arm span (cm)						
10 Reach (cm)						
11 Inside leg length (cm)						
12 Stride (cm)						
13 Foot length (cm)						
14 Shoe size (If you have a young children's shoe size, make this a negative number.)						

Once you have finished collecting the data, go to the computer and type it into the data file. When the whole class has typed in their data, try the following out, using the computer:

1 Look at the records. Whose record is listed first?
2 Order the records by **name**. Whose record is listed first now?
3 Search for your own record and print it out.
4 Find all the people who have brown eyes. How many are there?
5 Find all the people who have brown eyes and black hair. How many are there? How many people with brown eyes do not have black hair?
6 Draw a pie chart to show the different hair colours in your class. Print it out.
7 Draw a bar chart to show the heights of people in your class. Print it out.
8 What is the average height of people in your class?
9 Draw a scattergram to show the heights and masses of people on your class. Print it out. Do taller people have greater mass?
10 Use the computer to find out if people with longer legs have a longer stride.
11 Use the computer to find out if taller people have a longer reach.
12 Look at questions 10 and 11 again. In both these questions you are testing an idea (or hypothesis) using the data file. Think of an hypothesis of your own and then test it using the data file.

Active Teaching and Learning Approaches in Science

The Planets

Use the planet database on the computer, or the data sheet, to find out the information needed to do this activity.

What you need to do:

1 Copy out the table. Write in the names of the planets in our solar system. Start with the one nearest the sun.

Name of planet	Distance from the sun	Average surface temperature	Diameter of planet	Description of planet

2 Plot a graph to show the diameter of each planet against the distance from the sun. The planetary diameter should be on the vertical axis.

3 Plot a graph of the average surface temperature of each planet against the distance from the sun. The temperature should be on the vertical axis.

4 Can you see a link between the diameter of a planet and the distance from the sun? If there is a link, are there any exceptions? Explain any exceptions.

Is there any link between the average surface temperature of a planet and the distance from the sun? If there is a link, are there any exceptions? Explain any exceptions.

5 Use the information in the table to draw circles which represent the sun and the nine planets. Is it possible to draw the circles to scale?

6 Either:
  a Stick the sun in the middle of a piece of paper and arrange the planets around the sun. (Do this so that the distances between the planets and the sun are to scale.)

  Or:
  b Make a mobile by hanging the planets from the sun with pieces of cotton. The lengths of the pieces of cotton should represent the distance of each planet from the sun.

In each case, use the descriptions of the planets in the table to include the following details in your drawings:
– any colour,
– number of moons,
– the presence of any rings.

     Active Teaching and Learning Approaches in Science

THE PLANETS – DATA SHEET

Name of planet	Mean distance from the sun (millions km)	Time taken to orbit the sun once (yrs)	Diameter (km)	Rotation period (hours)	Number of times the mass of Earth	Average temperature (°C)	Escape velocity (km/s)	Atmosphere	Relative density	Number of moons	Description
Mercury	58	0.24	4878	1416	0.06	350	4.3	None	5.5	0	Has a rocky surface, which is covered with craters. The craters were formed by the impact of meteorites. High ridges (up to 2 km) have been created by the planet shrinking.
Venus	108	0.6	12103	5832	0.8	465	10.3	Thick carbon dioxide	5.2	0	Has a very hot, rocky surface, which is covered in clouds. The clouds contain sulphuric acid. The atmosphere has a high pressure, and there are thunderstorms. Huge mountains and volcanoes (larger than any on Earth), lowland plains and craters form the surface.
Earth	150	1	12756	24	1	15	11.2	Nitrogen and oxygen	5.5	1	Has a rocky surface, of which 70 per cent is covered in water. The planet is active, with earthquakes, volcanoes and moving crust, and it supports life. There is ice at the poles.
Mars	228	1.9	6794	24.6	0.11	–23	5	Thin carbon dioxide	3.9	2	The rocky surface has meteorite craters, very large volcanoes, and a large canyon named Valles Marinens. Mars has a red iron-rich soil, and thin clouds of carbon dioxide form frosts on the surface. There are dry river beds amongst the deserts, and icecaps at the poles.
Jupiter	778	11.9	142800	9.9	318	–150	59.5	Ammonia, water, hydrogen and helium	1.3	16	Jupiter is a gas giant. It has high clouds of frozen ammonia and water. A sea of liquid hydrogen and helium forms the planet centre. Jupiter has a faint ring system of orange bands separated by whitish zones. The Great Red Spot is the top of a storm, lasting over 300 years.
Saturn	1427	29.5	120000	10.6	95	–180	35.6	Hydrogen and helium	0.7	20	Saturn is a gas giant, with a strong ring system. The rings are made of rocks and dust, which are mostly covered in a fog of frozen ammonia. The planet consists of liquid hydrogen oceans.
Uranus	2870	84	52400	16	15	–210	21.2	Hydrogen and methane	1.3	15	Uranus is a blue gas giant. It is made of liquid hydrogen and helium oceans. Uranus has nine faint rings surrounding it.
Neptune	4500	165	50500	18	17	–220	23.6	Hydrogen and methane	1.7	8	Neptune is a blue gas giant, similar to Uranus and has four faint rings surrounding it.
Pluto	5900	248	2284	153.6	0.002	–220	5	Very thin methane	2.0	1	Pluto is the smallest planet in the solar system with a moon one-seventh as large as itself. It has a rocky surface, covered in frozen methane.

Active Teaching and Learning Approaches in Science

Sorting things

Your teacher will put a pile of objects at the front of the laboratory, which you will study during this exercise. At some time during the lesson your group will use a computer to help you find differences between the objects and make a **key** of your collection.

Scientists often put objects which are similar in some way into groups. For example, all metals together, all birds together, all plants together. In this way scientists sort or **classify** things. To do this we need to tell the difference between objects. This means we have to make **observations** about the different groups.

In your group, choose four objects from the collection. Each person in the group should then try to write down ten observations about one of the objects. When everybody has finished, look at each other's lists and see if you can add anything else.

Write the names of your objects on a sheet of display paper. Draw each object if you like. Write your list of descriptions underneath each object. Now use the 'branch' computer program to help you sort your objects.

Using 'Branch'

1 Hold down **shift** and **break** to load the program.

2 Press **A** to select **Branch**.

3 Press the **space bar**.

4 Select **2** to **Create a new tree.**

5 Type a title for your tree (this can be a word or a sentence).

6 Enter the number of objects.

7 Type in the name of each object, press **return** after each one.

8 Look at your list of descriptions for each object and write a question to separate your list into two groups. You must be able to answer the question with a **yes** or **no**, so start with:

> is it . . .
> does it . . .
> has it . . .
> can it . . . , etc.

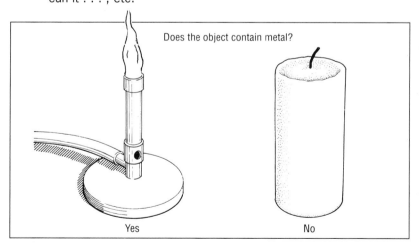

9 Answer the questions for each of your objects as asked by the computer.

10 When you have finished, press **1** to **use** the tree or press **4** to **look** and then **print** out your questions.

11 You may **save** your tree on the disk and then add to it later, press **5** and type in the name of your tree. This time it can only be up to seven letters long.

     Active Teaching and Learning Approaches in Science

Out on the trail

What you need to do:

Plan a field trip in your locality to produce a survey of all the different rocks used in building materials.

For each type of rock describe:

– where it is used,
– what it is used for,
– why you think it was chosen for that purpose.

Present your results in a table.

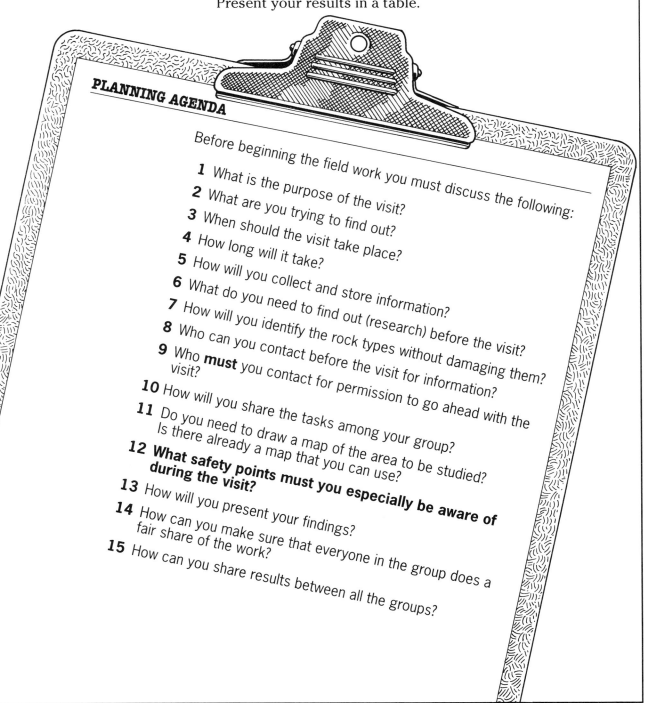

PLANNING AGENDA

Before beginning the field work you must discuss the following:

1 What is the purpose of the visit?
2 What are you trying to find out?
3 When should the visit take place?
4 How long will it take?
5 How will you collect and store information?
6 What do you need to find out (research) before the visit?
7 How will you identify the rock types without damaging them?
8 Who can you contact before the visit for information?
9 Who **must** you contact for permission to go ahead with the visit?
10 How will you share the tasks among your group?
11 Do you need to draw a map of the area to be studied? Is there already a map that you can use?
12 **What safety points must you especially be aware of during the visit?**
13 How will you present your findings?
14 How can you make sure that everyone in the group does a fair share of the work?
15 How can you share results between all the groups?

Noise patrol

You are an Environmental Health Officer for the council. The letter below has been handed to you:

34 Barkers Street
Sleep Town

10 September

The Environmental Health Officer
Town Hall
Market Square
Sleep Town

Dear Sir/Madam

I live in the centre of town, but I still think that the noise level is far too high. Constant traffic, road works, music and noisy neighbours are all too much. I'm sick of it. I don't know which of these is responsible for most of the noise, but I believe it is your job to find out. Please make a survey of the noise in the town centre as I would like to know which things cause most disturbance. Perhaps then you can do something about them.

I look forward to your reply.

Yours faithfully

A. Dinn

What you need to do:

Plan a visit to the local 'High Street' to carry out a noise survey. You must decide how you are going to measure the noises. Once you have completed the survey, respond to A. Dinn's letter.

Some things to think about:

- When will you visit the High Street?
- Do you have a noise meter or a tape recorder?
- How will you record your results and make sure that they are fair?
- How will you make your visit **safe**?

You may wish to use clue card A to help you plan your visit.

 Active Teaching and Learning Approaches in Science

Local noise problems – arranging a visitor

What you need to do:

Read the newspaper article and then answer the questions:

MANCHESTER AIRPORT, the third largest in Britain, is expanding rapidly.

Latest figures show that in the year ending March 1990 it had 10 million passengers and 155 305 aircraft movements. About 80 per cent of the time aircraft take off near Knutsford, to the south-west, but when the wind changes it affects the more densely populated areas of Cheadle, Stockport and Bramhall. Claire Donkin, a member of the Manchester Airport Joint Action Council (MAJAC), lives in Cheadle Hulme, three miles from the airport. 'Conversations in the garden are interrupted, bathroom cabinets shake and bottles fall out of shelves,' she says.

Night flights are a considerable problem: 'We have more charter night flights than Heathrow and Gatwick,' says Ms Donkin. Manchester's nightflight quota from April to October 1989 was 7098. But, says Ms Donkin, it regularly exceeds this. 'They don't include the noisy BA146 – they pretend it is so quiet it doesn't count.'

The airport, which spends £1m a year on noise insulation grants and

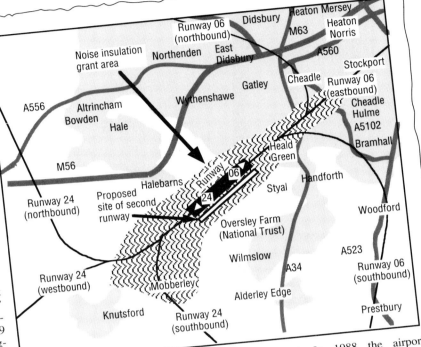

vortex damage, recently surveyed noise disturbance among people living nearby, but groups such as MAJAC were not included. In 1988 the airport received 534 noise complaints; last year the figure had increased to 2042.

---

1 How many passengers passed through Manchester airport in the year ending March 1990.

2 Which town is near the place where most of the flights take off? Circle it in red on the map.

3 Where are the most heavily populated areas around the airport? Circle them in blue on the map.

4 What problems caused by noise are mentioned in the article?

5 How many night flights were there from April to October, 1989?

6 Why do you think night flights cause local residents more problems than day flights?

7 Underline in red the number of complaints received by the airport in 1988.

8 Underline in blue the number of complaints received by the airport in 1989.

Your area

You may not live near an airport, but it is possible that your local Environmental Health Officer receives complaints about other types of noise. Why not ask them?

Invite an Environmental Health Officer to your school to help you with a topic on noise in your area. Use clue card B to help you with this.

CLUE CARD

Noise patrol

Before a visit, discuss and answer the following questions:

1 What are the reasons for the visit?

2 What 'science' do we intend to find out about during the visit?

3 Who can we contact before the visit for information? How can we contact them?

4 Can we design a checklist/worksheet of things to look out for?

5 What do we measure? How will we measure it?

6 How shall we record any useful information that we find?

7 What shall we do with all the information we collect?

8 How should we present our findings?

9 How will we know if the visit helped us to understand the topic better?

10 Could someone visit us at school to follow up the work with us?

CLUE CARD

Local noise problems – arranging a visitor

Before you invite a visitor to school, discuss and answer the following questions:

1 Who can we ask to visit?

2 What do we expect them to talk about?

3 How do we invite the visitor?

4 Where should the group meet the visitor?

5 Who should greet the visitor? How will this be done and where?

6 How long should the visit last?

7 Who will introduce the visitor and thank them at the end?

8 How will the visitor know what to talk about? How will they be told of the arrangements for the visit?

9 What questions do we need to ask? Should we prepare some questions for the visitor now, and send them to the visitor before they actually visit?

10 What room will we use and how will we arrange it? Do we need to provide refreshments?

11 How will we follow up the visit? What will we do with the new information we have?

     Active Teaching and Learning Approaches in Science

Crops and climate

The table shows the amount of rainfall each summer in India from 1959 to 1977 (except 1970). The table also shows the crop size for each year (except 1974).

Year	Rainfall (mm)	Crop size (million tonnes)
1959	750	560
1960	1005	750
1961	1055	755
1962	890	500
1963	1005	0
1964	1005	770
1965	500	625
1966	505	635
1967	1010	920
1968	630	915
1969	880	920
1970	?	1120
1971	890	1020
1972	505	1010
1973	650	740
1974	450	?
1975	900	1150
1976	750	1140

1 Plot the rainfall figures and the crop sizes on the vertical axis of the same graph (like the one shown here). You can use the same scale for both sets of figures, but plot each set in a different colour.

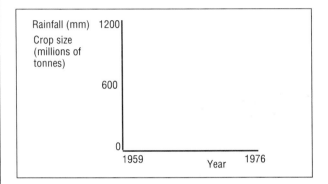

2 Use the graph you have drawn to estimate the missing results in the table. Complete the table.

3 Is there a link between rainfall and crop size? Is there anything in the shape of the two graphs which tells you this?

4 What other things might affect the size of a crop?

5 Could any of these things have led to no crop in 1963?

6 Read the passage below carefully and use the information to fill in the empty table.

Every crop requires a certain climate if it is to grow well. Farmers need to decide on the crop they grow, depending on their local climate. In India the heavy rainfalls and hot weather combine to make rice crops grow very well. Canada has hot summers also, but not as much rain. Wheat grows better in Canada. In southern England wheat and barley flourish in the warm, but wet climate. Oats, which prefer wet springs and cool summers, are the most common crop in Scotland.

Place	Climate	Crop

Active Teaching and Learning Approaches in Science

Who's the fitter?

Two 15-year-olds, Tracy and Jane, were arguing about fitness. Each girl thought she was fitter than the other. To settle the argument, they agreed to test themselves by sprinting 100 metres and measuring their pulse rates. They measured pulse rates at two-minute intervals from the start of the exercise, and for 16 minutes in total. Tracy and Jane decided to estimate their **recovery period**. This is the length of time from the end of an exercise to when the pulse rate returns to normal (**resting pulse**). Their results are shown in Table 1.

Table 1

Time (minutes)	Pulse rate (beats per minute)	
	Jane	Tracy
0	60	74
2	87	100
4	101	118
6	99	114
8	90	106
10	78	98
12	68	89
14	60	82
16	60	74

Plot Tracy's and Jane's pulse rates on **one** graph. Use the graph to answer these questions:

1 What was Jane's maximum pulse rate and what was Tracy's maximum pulse rate?
2 What is the difference (in beats per minute) between each of their resting pulse rates and their maximum pulse rates?
3 Estimate both girls' recovery periods.
4 Who is the fitter of the two girls? Give **two** reasons for your answer.

An hour or so after the sprint, Tracy got severe cramp in her right calf muscle. Her parents were concerned, because she regularly got cramp after doing heavy physical exercise. However, Tracy attends an aerobics class every week and does not suffer from cramp after that. Tracy's parents took her to the doctor, who sent her to the hospital for tests. At the hospital she was asked to do some heavy exercises and the nurses took blood samples at regular intervals afterwards. The blood samples were analysed and the results are show in Table 2.

Table 2

Time after finishing exercise (minutes)	Levels of substance in blood (arbitrary units)			
	Oxygen	Glucose	Lactic acid	Fatty acids
1	60	40	0	26
2	0	16	0	27
3	11	8	6	26
4	31	22	17	25
5	60	34	32	25

Plot **all four** sets of results on **one** graph. Use the graph to answer these questions:

5 Why did the level of oxygen in the blood go down and then up again?
6 Why does the level of glucose in the blood go down and then up?
7 One of the four substances is the cause of Tracy's cramp. Which one do you think it is? Explain your choice.
8 Where is the substance you gave in question 7 made?
9 Find out what the word 'aerobic' means.
10 Why doesn't Tracy get cramp after her aerobics class?
11 What other results would you need to see in order to be more certain about your conclusions?

 Active Teaching and Learning Approaches in Science

Can I stop in time?

Cars have a greater stopping distance at high speeds, than at low speeds. The *Highway Code* gives information about this. Look at Table 1.

Table 1

Speed of car (m/s)	A Distance travelled while driver moves foot to brake pedal (m)	B Distance travelled while brakes are on (m)
9	6	6
13	9	14
18	?	24
22	15	?
27	18	55
31	?	74

1 Plot two curves on the same graph to show how far a car travels once the driver decides to brake (distances A and B). What do you notice about the two curves? How is the **total stopping distance** worked out?

2 Copy out table 1 and complete it by filling in the missing figures.

3 The car in the picture is travelling at 18 m/s. The driver sees a fallen tree 30 m ahead.

   a How far will the car travel while the driver moves the foot to the brake pedal?

   b How much further will the car travel after the brakes are on?

   c Will the car hit the tree?

Table 2 shows some of the factors which increase the total stopping distance. Copy out the table. Complete it by explaining **why** the total stopping distance is increased.

Table 2

Factor	Reason why total stopping distance is increased
Alcohol consumption by driver	
Worn tyres	
Worn brake shoes	
Wet roads	
Loose chippings on the road surface	

Active Teaching and Learning Approaches in Science

A new scoreboard?

Pixels

Look at the pictures A, B and C. Picture A is of a normal photograph. The photograph has a range of shades between black and white. It is called an **analogue** copy. If we want to store the picture on a computer, we must convert the photograph to a **digital** form.

To convert the picture to a digital form, it must be broken down into little blocks called **pixels**. Each pixel must then be coded with either a **1** (if it is dark) or a **0** (if it is light). Moving across the picture (or pixels) is called **scanning**. Looking at individual pixels is called **sampling.**

Picture B was produced by scanning picture A, sampling each pixel, and coding it either 1 or 0. Picture B is made up of over a thousand pixels, which are either black (1) or white (0). Picture C is produced in the same way except that it has been sampled more frequently. The picture is therefore made up of many more, smaller pixels.

Many signs and scoreboards at sports matches and pop concerts are digital displays. They are made up of thousands of light bulbs arranged in a grid, which are either on or off. The light bulbs are the pixels here.

A major football club wants to build a new digital scoreboard. The scoreboard must show pictures clearly, but the club can afford to spend only £10 000 on it. There are four sizes of pixel to choose from. The larger pixels cost more, but less of them are needed to fill the scoreboard. The scoreboard will be 6 metres high and 7 metres wide.

Picture A

Picture B

Picture C

The four choices of scoreboard

Scoreboard	Pixel size	Number of pixels needed to fill scoreboard	Cost of each pixel (£)	Total cost of pixels for scoreboard (£)
A	100 cm 3 100 cm		40	
B	50 cm 3 50 cm		20	
C	20 cm 3 20 cm		10	
D	10 cm 3 10 cm		5	

1 Look at the table. Work out the number of pixels needed for each of the scoreboards A, B, C and D. Write your answers in the table.

2 Now work out the total cost of the pixels needed for each scoreboard. Write your answers in the table.

© Sheffield City Polytechnic/CollinsEducational 1992 *Active Teaching and Learning Approaches in Science*

If you look at the cost of each scoreboard, you will see that some are cheaper than others. However, does this mean they give as good a picture?

3 Look at the grids labelled A, B, C and D. They represent the pixels for each of the scoreboards. In turn, lay each grid (scoreboard) over the picture of the trophy, and carefully shade in each box (pixel) which has a line from the trophy passing through it. (You may need to hold the pieces of paper up to a window, while you do this.)

The football club employs you to advise them about what sort of pixel to choose for their scoreboard.

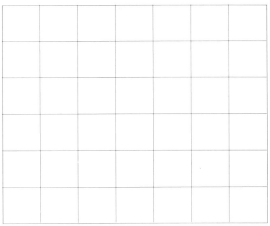

A

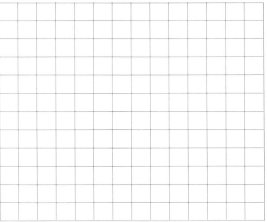

B

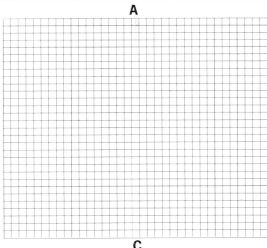

C

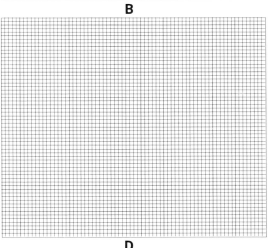

D

4 Look at the costs you have worked out and the quality of the pictures each scoreboard produces. Decide what pixel you think the football club should use.

5 Write a report to the football club. Your report should include the following:

- the name and address of your firm,

- an explanation of how the scoreboard works (try to use the words printed in bold),

- the results of your research (the numbers you have written in the table, and the four pictures of the trophy using each grid),

- your conclusions and advice to the football club (give reasons for the type of pixel you choose).

6 As you use more and more pixels, how do you think this will affect the type (and cost) of the computer needed to control a scoreboard?

Blue Crystal Ltd

Your group is a small research team in a chemical factory. Your job is to solve scientific problems. You receive a memo from your director. Read the memo together with the rest of your group and decide how you will solve the problem.

MEMO

Dear Team

It has come to my attention that we have a problem in the factory. As you are well aware, our process depends a lot on getting copper sulphate crystals to dissolve in water. At present this is taking too long and costing us a lot of money.

I understand from the report I have been given that you currently use cold water and crystals that are 1 cm long. I want you to look at ways to get the crystals to dissolve faster. Naturally, I would like to see a report from you on this by the end of the week!

Yours faithfully

I Lead

Budget rules sheet

Your research team will start with a budget of £100 000. During your research you may be asked to subtract costs from your budget or gain the chance to earn profits.

Before you begin **any** investigations, you must get your plan checked by your teacher. Wear safety goggles and remember that copper sulphate is harmful.

Your final report should include the following:
– what you were trying to do,
– what you did,
– what your results were,
– what recommendations you will give your director,
– your completed accounts sheet.

Costs (subtract these from your budget)	£
Every time you ask for help	5 000
Every chemical you spill or piece of apparatus you break	20 000
A false start or unfair testing	50 000
Dangerous techniques, e.g. no safety goggles	50 000

Profits (add these to your budget)	£
The production of a detailed plan	10 000
Experiments carried out safely	50 000
Final report of the project – on time	200 000

Date:

ACCOUNT SHEET

Name(s) of researcher(s):

Costs	Amount	Profits	Amount	Balance
				£100 000

Active Teaching and Learning Approaches in Science

Hot cans

You work for a research company. You have recently received this letter:

Hot Can Company
25 Walnut Grove
Cowley
Oxford

24 October

Research Team
Clever Chemicals
Greenford Industrial Estate
Greenford

Dear Research Team,

We are a small company involved in manufacturing canned food and we are looking into the possibility of producing self-heating cans. The scientific idea behind the method of heating the 'Hot Can' is very simple. It is probably known to you. When water is added to lime a great deal of heat is given out. We are looking for a lime supplier, and have narrowed this down to three companies.

I enclose three samples of lime from the companies, labelled A, B and C. We would like you to test each sample to see which one gives out most heat when mixed with a small quantity of water.

We would like you to send us a report describing what tests you did and what you found out.

Yours sincerely

A. Jones
General Manager

Plan an investigation to find out which sample, A, B or C, gives out the most heat when mixed with a quantity of water. You will need to think about the following when you are planning your investigation:

– What will you measure?
– How will you measure it?
– What will you keep the same, to make sure the tests are fair?
– What apparatus will you need?
– Safety (use less than 5g of each sample).

Before you carry out your investigation, get your plan checked by a teacher. Write a report to the Hot Can Company.

What a waste

You work for an advertising agency and have received a letter from the local Borough Council.

Alton Borough Council
Recycling office
Harwood Avenue
London SW6

10 May

The Advertising Director
Easy Speak Advertising
Cassette House
Holborn
London WC1

Dear Sir/Madam

Radio advertisement for council recycling scheme

In order to publicise the recycling collection facilities which we are currently offering in the borough, Alton Council plan to broadcast a 3-minute radio advertisement. Your company has been selected to produce the advert and we would like to hear a demo tape of what points you plan to include.

Please can I ask you to prepare the demo tape by the end of the month. I look forward to hearing your suggestions,

Yours faithfully

A Patel
Council recycling officer

It is your next team meeting and you must discuss the points listed in the agenda. Do this in your group. Once you have done this, prepare a script for the radio broadcast requested in the letter. Remember, the broadcast should last no longer than 3 minutes.

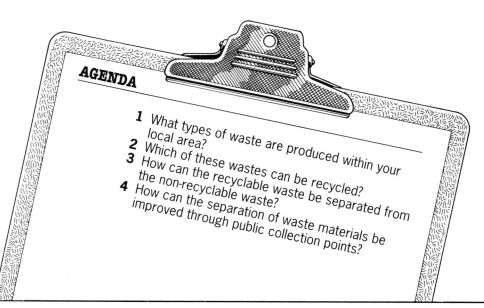

AGENDA

1 What types of waste are produced within your local area?
2 Which of these wastes can be recycled?
3 How can the recyclable waste be separated from the non-recyclable waste?
4 How can the separation of waste materials be improved through public collection points?

    Active Teaching and Learning Approaches in Science

Fossil evidence

A radio reporter has just had a nasty shock. The reporter had completed an interview on the subject of fossils, with a famous scientist, when it was discovered that one of the microphones was not working. None of the scientists' answers have been recorded!

How can you help?

1 Read this copy of the interview:

Interviewer Hello ladies and gentlemen, and welcome to another programme in the series *Geology Matters*. We are pleased to have Dr Brown with us today, who is a leading expert on the subject of fossils. Dr Brown, hello.

Dr Brown *?*

Interviewer Perhaps you would start by explaining to the listeners what a fossil is.

Dr Brown *?*

Interviewer We all know that animals and plants rot after they die. How are fossils preserved?

Dr Brown *?*

Interviewer That's very interesting, but how can you be sure that fossils are as old as you claim they are?

Dr Brown *?*

Interviewer Some rocks do not have any fossils in them at all. Why is that, Dr Brown?

Dr Brown *?*

Interviewer I read somewhere that more sea creatures form fossils than land creatures. Can you explain why this happens?

Dr Brown *?*

Interviewer What type of creatures were the first ones to be preserved as fossils? How old are they?

Dr Brown *?*

Interviewer That seems very old. How old is the Earth thought to be?

Dr Brown *?*

Interviewer Why are there no fossils of the first animals on Earth?

Dr Brown *?*

Interviewer Some rocks contain more fossils than others. What does this tell us about the place where the rocks were formed?

Dr Brown *?*

Interviewer I've heard that some types of rock are made up almost entirely of fossil remains. Which rocks are these?

Dr Brown *?*

Interviewer Fossils are used to find out how old rocks are. How is this done?

Dr Brown *?*

Interviewer Finally Dr Brown, why are coal and oil sometimes called fossil fuels?

Dr Brown *?*

Interviewer Thank you very much Dr Brown. Next week listeners, we will be talking about volcanoes and earthquakes.
Until then, goodbye.

2 In your group, discuss, and then write down, the answers you think Dr Brown would have given.

What next?

3 When you have worked out what you think Dr Brown said, make a tape recording of the interview. Swop your tape with a recording made by another group.

4 Listen to the tape you are given. Do you think the other group's answers are correct?

5 Write brief comments on the recording you are given, as if you were reviewing the programme for a local newspaper.

Active Teaching and Learning Approaches in Science

Powerful stuff

Find the words missing from the sentences below and write them into the crossword.

Across

4 Electricity is _____ stuff. (8)

6 Being _____ with electricity, even for a minute, could kill you. (8)

8 If you are carrying a long object, watch out for overhead electricity _____. (6)

10 You don't have to _____ an electric cable to get a shock. (5)

11 The warning signs are for _____ safety. (4)

12 Keep a safe _____ from electricity cables, pylons and generators. (8)

Down

1 _____ is an essential part of our daily lives. (11)

2 Be _____ of the possible dangers around you! (5)

3 Electricity can jump across _____ as sparks. (4)

4 If you lose something on or near cables, call the _____. (6)

5 Treat electricity with _____. (7)

7 Warning signs are deadly _____. (7)

9 Think _____ when you are dealing with electricity. (4)

Use all the words from the crossword to write a story for a younger brother, sister or friend. The story should contain the message that electricity should be treated with respect. Underline the words you use from the crossword.

   Active Teaching and Learning Approaches in Science

Electrolysis

The Simulation

Read the following notes carefully. You are going to take part in a simulation. It will show you how molten sodium chloride conducts electricity during **electrolysis**.

The electrolysis of sodium chloride produces sodium and chlorine. Electricity is passed through the sodium chloride, which is called the **electrolyte.**

During the simulation you will either be an anode, a cathode, a battery, a chloride ion or a sodium ion. Your teacher will switch the room light on and off. When the light is on, the battery electricity is on, and you will act your role. When the light is switched off, you **must** stop moving.

What you need to do:

Once you have been given your role sheet, you will need to read it very carefully. You may want to practise your role with somebody else, who has the same role.

You will act out your role during the electrolysis simulation. **Don't** do anything else, other than what is on your role sheet.

Chloride ion
I need a chloride ion badge, a chlorine gas card and an electron card.

I am a chloride ion. I have a **negative** charge.

At the start of the simulation, I will move slowly around the middle of the room. When the electricity (room light) is switched on, I will move very slowly towards the **anode**. When I reach the

anode, I will wait for another **chloride ion** to arrive. I will then give my electron to the anode, and link arms with the other chloride ion.

Together we will be **chlorine gas**. We will sit together at the front of the room, and hold up the chlorine gas card.

Sodium ion
I need a sodium ion badge and a sodium metal card.

I am a sodium ion. I have a **positive** charge. At the start of the simulation, I will move slowly around the middle of the room. When the electricity (room light) is switched on, I will move very slowly towards the **cathode**.

When I reach the cathode I will wait for the cathode to give me an electron card. I will then be a **sodium metal atom**. I will sit down by the cathode, and hold up a sodium metal card.

Cathode
I need a cathode badge.

I am a cathode. I am the **negatively** charged electrode and made of graphite.

At the start I will be standing on the cathode spot. When the electricity

(room light) is switched on, I will stay where I am. I will wait for the battery to pass electron cards to me. I will give one electron card to each sodium atom that comes to me.

Anode
I will need an anode badge.

I am an anode. I am the **positively** charged electrode and made of graphite.

At the start I will be standing on the anode spot. When the electricity

(room light) is switched on, I will stay where I am. I will wait for chlorine ions to give me electron cards. I will pass these to the battery.

Battery
I will need a battery badge.

At the start I will stand on the battery spot. When the electricity (roomlight) is switched on, I will wait for electron cards to be given to me by the **anode**. I will pass electron cards to the **cathode**.

States of matter

The game

The game you are going to play looks at how substances can be divided into the three **states**: solids, liquids and gases.

1 The game is for two, three or four players.
2 The 24 dominoes are shuffled and divided equally between the players.
3 One player starts by laying any domino down, face up.
4 The player to the left plays the next domino so that the substance or state on the new domino matches with a substance or state on the first domino.
5 The game continues with players matching the dominoes in their hand with the dominoes that have already been laid.

6 If a player cannot match a domino they must 'knock' and allow the player to their left to continue the game.
7 Play continues in this way until one player has played all their dominoes.
8 Any player may challenge another player if they think that a substance does not match a state. The match should be checked (a teacher can help with this) and if the match is wrong the player who laid the wrong domino loses their turn **and** 4 points. If the match is correct then the player who made the challenge loses 4 points.

Scoring

1 Every time a domino is put down the player adds up the total number of dots shown on the substance and the state they have just matched. For example:

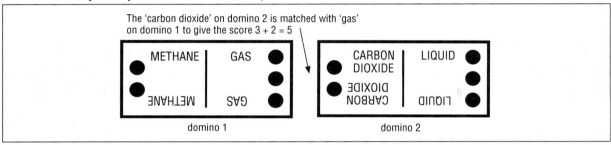

The 'carbon dioxide' on domino 2 is matched with 'gas' on domino 1 to give the score 3 + 2 = 5

2 If a player can match a substance with a state **and** match the number of dots, they receive double the total number of dots in points. For example:

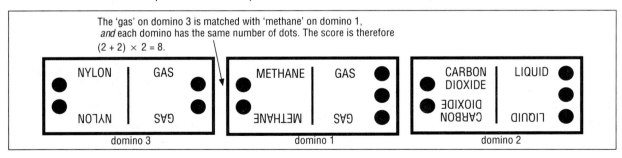

The 'gas' on domino 3 is matched with 'methane' on domino 1, *and* each domino has the same number of dots. The score is therefore (2 + 2) × 2 = 8.

3 At the end of the game the total number of dots on the remaining dominoes held by each player needs to be taken away from their score.

4 The player to lay down their dominoes first receives 10 bonus points.

5 The winner is the player who has the most points, and not the player who lays down their dominoes first.

Solo game

The dominoes can be used to play 'solo' states of matter, if you like. One person on their own can try to form a complete circle with the dominoes, and at the same time try to get the highest score.

    Active Teaching and Learning Approaches in Science

States of matter: dominoes

ICE — GAS	ICE — GAS	LEAD — LIQUID	LEAD — LIQUID	HYDROGEN — SOLID	HYDROGEN — SOLID	PETROL — SOLID	PETROL — SOLID	CHLORINE — LIQUID	CHLORINE — LIQUID	NYLON — GAS	NYLON — GAS

LEMONADE — SOLID	LEMONADE — SOLID	CARBON DIOXIDE — LIQUID	CARBON DIOXIDE — LIQUID	WATER — GAS	WATER — GAS	STEAM — SOLID	STEAM — SOLID	SILVER — GAS	SILVER — GAS	PARAFFIN — SOLID	PARAFFIN — SOLID

BLEACH — GAS	BLEACH — GAS	TIN — SOLID	TIN — SOLID	IRON — LIQUID	IRON — LIQUID	GOLD — LIQUID	GOLD — LIQUID	COPPER — SOLID	COPPER — SOLID	NITROGEN — SOLID	NITROGEN — SOLID

METHANE — GAS	METHANE — GAS	AIR — SOLID	AIR — SOLID	DIAMOND — LIQUID	DIAMOND — LIQUID	BRICK — LIQUID	BRICK — LIQUID	VINEGAR — GAS	VINEGAR — GAS	MILK — SOLID	MILK — SOLID

Enzyme action – lock and key model

Enzymes

Enzymes are catalysts that speed up the chemical reactions in the cells of organisms. Enzymes are very important to organisms since without enzymes the reactions would happen too slowly.

Enzymes are different to ordinary catalysts like manganese dioxide. The main difference is that enzymes have a special shape. The special shape includes an **active site** which fits around the molecule the enzyme is helping to react – rather like a lock fits around a key.

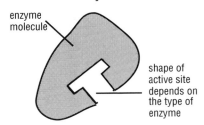

The enzyme that catalyses the reaction between maltose and water in the body to produce glucose is called **maltase**:

$$\text{maltose} + \text{water} \xrightleftharpoons{\text{maltase}} \text{glucose} + \text{glucose}$$

Maltose is simply two glucose molecules joined together. Maltase splits the maltose molecules into the two glucose molecules. The maltose molecule is called the **substrate** and the glucose molecules are called the **products**. The active site of the maltase molecule fits the maltose molecule exactly. Maltase can therefore only break up maltose molecules. Maltase is the key that unlocks maltose molecules.

How does an enzyme work?

1 Find two different pieces of coloured card or paper, a pair of scissors, some glue and a piece of white A4 paper.
2 Choose one piece of coloured card (or paper) and draw shape A on to it. Make sure you use exactly the same measurements. Cut out shape A and label it 'maltose'. Do this again so that you have two maltose molecules.

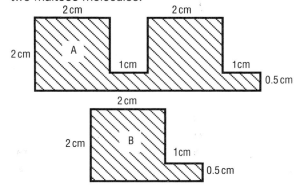

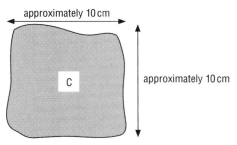

3 Using the same coloured card as the maltose molecules, draw shape B and cut it out. Label this 'glucose'. Do this again so that you have two glucose molecules.
4 Using the other coloured card (or paper) cut out a piece of paper that looks something like shape C. Use this as a template to make two more of these. Label each of them 'maltase'.
5 Now cut out the shape of the active site for each of the maltase molecules. Think of the shape of the maltose molecules to help you with this. Read the notes on enzymes again if you are not sure what to do.
6 Turn the piece of plain paper on its side and write on it "How an enzyme works". Under this heading copy out the following equation right across the top of the page:

$$\begin{matrix} \text{enzyme} \\ + \\ \text{substrate} \end{matrix} \xrightleftharpoons{} \begin{matrix} \text{enzyme/substrate} \\ \text{complex} \end{matrix} \xrightleftharpoons{} \begin{matrix} \text{enzyme} \\ + \\ \text{products} \end{matrix}$$

7 Stick the molecules you have made on to the plain paper so that they follow the equation.
8 Underneath the diagram describe how the enzyme maltase breaks maltose into two glucose molecules.
9 The diagram below shows the breakdown of a protein chain by the enzyme protease. Is there anything wrong with the diagram?

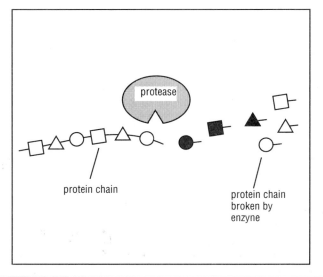

© Sheffield City Polytechnic/CollinsEducational 1992   *Active Teaching and Learning Approaches in Science*

Bibliography

Language in Science, Study Series No. 16, ASE, 1980

Baldwin, Jill and Wells, Harry (ed.) *Active Tutorial Work Book 1: The First Year*, Blackwell, 1979

Baldwin, Jill and Wells, Harry (ed.) *Active Tutorial Work Book 2: The Second Year*, Blackwell, 1979

Baldwin Jill and Wells, Harry (ed.) *Active Tutorial Work Book 3: The Third Year*, Blackwell, 1980

Baldwin, Jill and Wells, Harry (ed.) *Active Tutorial Work Book 4: The Fourth Year*, Blackwell, 1980

Baldwin, Jill and Wells, Harry (ed.) *Active Tutorial Work Book 5: The Fifth Year*, Blackwell, 1981

Beer, S., Edwards, D., Jackson, R., *Thinking Through Science: Activities from Chemistry 1*, Edwards, D., (ed), Collins Educational, 1989

Bentley, D. and Watts, M., *Learning and Teaching in School Science. Practical Alternatives*, Open University Press, 1989

Boyd, J., Whitelaw, W., *Understanding Science 1*, John Murray, 1989

Brandes, D. and Ginnis, P., M., *A Guide to Student-Centred Learning*, Blackwell, 1986

Brandes, D. and Phillips, M., *Gamesters' Handbook*, Hutchinson, 1978

Bulman, L., *Teaching Language and Study Skills In Secondary Science*, Heinemann, 1985

Burrows, P., *GCSE Questions on Everyday Chemistry*, Blackie, 1988

Coles. M., Gott, R., and Thornley, T., *Active Science 1*, Collins Educational, 1988

Coles. M., Gott, R., and Thornley, T., *Active Science 2*, Collins Educational, 1989

Croner's Manual for Heads of Science, Croner Publications Ltd, 1988

Davies, F. and Green, T., *Reading for Learning in the Sciences*, Oliver and Boyd, 1984

Foster, S., *Streetwise Physics, SSR, Vol.71, No.254*, 1989

Gardner, K. and Lunzer, E.A., (eds) *Effective Use of Reading*, Heinemann Educational, 1979

Gott, R., Price, G., and Thornley, T., *Active Science 3*, Collins Educational, 1991

Gott, R., Foulds, K., Feasey, R., Pryke, T., and Robeley, I., *Science in Action Key Stage 3*, Blackie, 1990

Harrison, W., 'Games, Simulations and Case Studies as Learning Resources', *The Association for Science Education Study Series No. 14: Resource-Based Learning in Science*, ASE, 1978

Honey, P. and Mumford, A., *Using Your Learning Skills*, P Honey, 1986

Hopson, B., and Scally, M., *Life Skills Teaching Programme. No. 3*, Life Skill Associates, 1986

Johnston, K., *CLIS News 2, CLIS*, 1987

Jones, K., *Designing Your Own Simulations*, Methuen, 1985

Lock, R., *School Science Review, Vol. 71, No.256*, 1990

Olejnk, I., *Biology in Daily Life*, Blackie, 1988

Smith, T., Tear, C., and Yate, A., *Thinking Through Science: Activities from Physics 1*, Edwards, D. (ed.), Collins Educational, 1989

SSCR, *Better Science: Approaches to Teaching and Learning. Curriculum Guide 4*, Heinemann Educational/ASE, 1987

SSCR (Sheffield Working Group), *Biotech*, ASE, 1987

SSCR (Wiltshire), *Science Think Books: an introduction to their use in Science Lessons*, ASE

Van Ments, M., *The Effective Use of Role Play. A Handbook for Teachers and Trainers*, Kogan Page, 1983

Watts, M., *The Science of Problem Solving. A Practical Guide for Science Teachers*, Heinemann, 1991

Wellington, J.J., *The Nuclear Issue*, Blackwell, 1986

Index